The Niki Davies Calendar of Songs

	Page	CD Track (Vocal | Backing)	
LYRICS & TEACHER'S NOTES	2	-	
THE SONGS			
It's A New Year	22	1	21
Dragon Dance	24	2	22
Valentine	26	3	23
There's A Pancake On The Ceiling!	28	4	24
Can You Think Of A Word?	30	5	25
Have A Day Off, Mum	32	6	26
There's A Bear In The Fridge	34	7	27
It's The London Marathon	36	8	28
Maypole	38	9	29
Friend To The World	40	10	30
It's An Easy Thing To Do	42	11	31
It's Father's Day	44	12	32
Are You Ready For Some Summer Fun?	46	13	33
In My Book	48	14	34
Thank You For The Harvest	50	15	35
Crunching Through The Leaves	52	16	36
Wear A Poppy Today	54	17	37
Give A Little Smile	56	18	38
Behind The Window	58	19	39
Happy Christmas!	60	20	40
COPYRIGHT INFORMATION	63		

Please log our songs on your CWCL or CCL copy report

IT'S A NEW YEAR

(January)

1 It's a new year, it's really here,
Hello everyone.
It's a new year, it's really here,
So welcome, welcome,
Welcome to you.

2 It's chilly out there, but we don't care,
Hello everyone.
It's chilly out there, but we don't care,
So welcome, welcome,
Welcome to you.

3 It's a new term and we've lots to learn,
Hello everyone.
It's a new term and we've lots to learn,
So welcome, welcome,
Welcome to you.

4 It's a new year, it's really here,
Hello everyone.
It's a new year, it's really here,
So welcome, welcome,
Welcome to you.
So welcome, welcome,
Welcome to you.

Teacher's Notes

- A great song to welcome in any new year and settle the children back into the nursery/school routine. Try and think up some hand movements that the children can enjoy for the 'welcome, welcome' bit of the song.
- Talk about New Year celebrations. What sorts of traditions do we keep to welcome in the new year? Did any of the children sing 'Auld Lang Syne' over the holiday? Do the children know of any other traditions from around the world for this time of year? (There are some quite peculiar ones if you have a look online!)

Dragon Dance

(Chinese New Year: January/February)

1 Here comes the dragon dancing down the street,
Here comes the dragon, see his bouncing feet.
Rising up to the sky,
Swooping down from on high,
See him leap, see him prance,
Doing the dragon dance.

2 Here comes the dragon dancing down the street,
Here comes the dragon, see his bouncing feet.
Hear the sound of the gong
As he dances along,
See him leap, see him prance,
Doing the dragon dance.

3 Here comes the dragon dancing down the street,
Here comes the dragon, see his bouncing feet.
Silver scales bright as day,
And the drum beats away,
See him leap, see him prance,
Doing the dragon dance.

4 Repeat verse 1

Teacher's Notes

- Chinese music can sound very distinctive. This is because it is often based around just five notes (called the pentatonic scale) and played on instruments that we don't use that often in western music. Listen to the song with the children and see if they can hear the different instruments at the beginning of the song – and the gong at the end.
- Make some Chinese Dragons with the children: use painted egg boxes for the mouth, and cut out two more egg cups for the eyes. Paint these white with a black dot in the centre of each and stick them on the lid of the first egg box. Take a strip of thin coloured card (about the same width as the egg box) and concertina-fold it all the way along for the dragon's body. Attach this to the back of the head. Then take some strips of tissue paper and glue these to the edge of the body, to dangle down and create more movement. Use any other scraps from your craft cupboard to add more decoration and personality.
- Whilst singing the song, encourage the children to mirror the words with their homemade dancing dragons.

(14 February)

1 I'm going to draw a big, red heart,
That's what I'm going to do.
I'm going to draw a big, red heart
To show that I love you.
Valentine, valentine,
Will you be my valentine?

2 I'm going to make a great big card
And put the heart inside.
I'm going to make a great big card
And paint it nice and bright.
Valentine, valentine,
Will you be my valentine?

3 I'm going to write some words inside
And they will say, 'Guess who?'
I'm going to write some words inside
Then give the card to you.
Valentine, valentine,
Will you be my valentine?

Teacher's Notes

- Hearts are difficult shapes to draw because it's hard to make the curved lines symmetrical. Look at other shapes and see if they are symmetrical. Can the children work out where the lines of symmetry are for different shapes? Is there ever more than one line of symmetry? How many lines of symmetry does a heart shape have?
- Why not try painting half a heart (using lots of paint) and then fold the paper over, pressing down firmly so the paint is transferred to make the other half of the heart. You can achieve all sorts of swirly effects by mixing in different colours.
- Traditionally, poetry was given to a sweetheart as a sign of love and affection. Have a look at the lyrics from the song and see if the children can identify the rhyming words. Can they think up some more and write a simple poem in the cards that they make for their valentine?

There's a Pancake on the Ceiling!

(Shrove Tuesday: February/March)

1 There's a pancake on the ceiling, oh dear!
There's a pancake on the ceiling, oh dear!
Now this is kind of funny, 'cos it should be in my tummy,
A pancake's on the ceiling, oh dear!

2 There's a pancake on the window, oh dear!
There's a pancake on the window, oh dear!
Now this is kind of funny, 'cos it should be in my tummy,
A pancake's on the window, oh dear!

3 There's a pancake in the fish tank, oh dear!
There's a pancake in the fish tank, oh dear!
Now this is kind of funny, 'cos it should be in my tummy,
A pancake's in the fish tank, oh dear!

4 There's a pancake on the kettle, oh dear!
There's a pancake on the kettle, oh dear!
Now this is kind of funny, 'cos it should be in my tummy,
A pancake's on the kettle, oh dear!

5 There's a pancake on the budgie, oh dear!
There's a pancake on the budgie, oh dear!
Now this is kind of funny, 'cos it should be in my tummy,
A pancake's on the budgie, oh dear!

Teacher's Notes

- To continue the theme of cooking, why not add some kitchen percussion to this song? Bring in a selection of kitchen utensils, or ask the children to bring in an object from their own kitchen that they can use to make a sound. Hopefully you will end up with a selection of instruments to make clanging, banging, ringing, scraping and jingling sounds.
- Start by clapping along in time to the song – can the children find the beat? Some will find this easier than others. Select some of the instruments that make a solid sound (rather than ones that echo or rattle) and use these to play along to the song on the beat.
- Next, listen to the backing track on the CD and see what other sounds you can hear. An amusing way to do this is to have all the children sitting on the floor – when they hear a fun sound they should stand up, and then sit down again until the next one. Have another look at your kitchen instruments and select some that might make fun sounds that you can include at certain points in the song. Perhaps a rotary hand whisk or some cutlery rattled in a pot.

CAN YOU THINK OF A WORD?

(World Poetry Day: 21 March)

1 Can you think of a word that rhymes with 'cat'?
Can you think of a word? It could be 'mat'.
I think a good one would be 'bat'
Because it rhymes with 'cat'.

2 Can you think of a word that rhymes with 'pig'?
Can you think of a word? It could be 'fig'.
I think a good one would be 'dig'
Because it rhymes with 'pig'.

3 Can you think of a word that rhymes with 'pet'?
Can you think of a word? It could be 'vet'.
I think a good one would be 'wet'
Because it rhymes with 'pet'.

4 Can you think of a word that rhymes with 'dot'?
Can you think of a word? It could be 'pot'.
I think a good one would be 'lot'
Because it rhymes with 'dot'.

5 Can you think of a word that rhymes with 'nut'?
Can you think of a word? It could be 'hut'.
I think a good one would be 'but'
Because it rhymes with 'nut'.

Teacher's Notes

- What a fabulously useful song this is, giving you tons of mileage for making up new verses and getting the children to concentrate on rhyming words.
- Give each child a letter and then call out a simple word and ask them to hold up their letter if they can start a word that rhymes with the one you've just called out.
- Transfer what the children have learnt with their rhymes into a 'poetry picture'. Ask the children to choose their favourite verse and draw a picture that includes images of all the rhyming words from the verse, along with more things that have the same rhyme.

HAVE A DAY OFF, MUM

(Mother's Day: March/April)

1 Have a day off, Mum, have a day off.
It will be okay.
Have a day off 'cos I love you
And because it's Mother's Day.

2 Go and sit down, Mum, go and sit down.
It will be okay.
Go and sit down 'cos I love you
And because it's Mother's Day.

3 I can be good, Mum, I can be good.
It will be okay.
I can be good 'cos I love you
And because it's Mother's Day.

4 Repeat verse 1

Teacher's Notes

- Can the children think of some things their mums do for them every day? What small things could the children do for their mums on Mother's Day to make them smile.
- Which other people help us in our day-to-day lives? (Other family, teachers, shopkeepers, dustbin men, lollipop ladies, etc.)
- Mother's Day is a good chance for your mum to have a day off. What kinds of things do people like to do on their days off?

There's a Bear in the Fridge

(April Fool's Day: 1 April)

1 Mum, there's a bear in the fridge,
Mum, there's a bear in the fridge.
It's right there, look if you dare,
There's a bear in the fridge!

2 Dad, there's a donkey in the car,
Dad, there's a donkey in the car.
It's right there, look if you dare,
There's a donkey in the car!

3 Gran, there's a frog on your head,
Gran, there's a frog on your head.
It's right there, look if you dare,
There's a frog on your head!

4 Help! There's a dragon in the bath.
Help! There's a dragon in the bath.
It's right there, look if you dare,
There's a dragon in the bath!

Teacher's Notes

- April Fool's Day is a tradition celebrated in many different countries where people play all kinds of jokes on one another. In some countries such as the UK, Canada and New Zealand, the jokes only last until midday, after which anyone who plays a joke is the fool. Elsewhere jokes can last all day. In France, children put paper fish on each other's back as a trick and shout 'poisson d'avril!'.
- Make some colourful paper fish and have fun practising the French tradition of 'poisson d'avril' on 1 April.

It's the London Marathon

(April)

1 Running, running, never stopping,
Running down the street.
Running, running, never stopping,
Lots and lots of feet.
It's the marathon,
It's the London* marathon.

2 Jogging, jogging, don't go stopping,
Jogging down the street.
Jogging, jogging, don't go stopping,
Lots and lots of feet.
It's the marathon,
It's the London marathon.

3 Puffing, puffing, nearly stopping,
Puffing down the street.
Puffing, puffing, nearly stopping,
Lots and lots of feet.
It's the marathon,
It's the London marathon.

4 Running, running, never stopping,
Running down the street.
Running, running, never stopping,
Lots and lots of feet.
It's the marathon,
It's the London marathon.
It's the marathon,
It's the London marathon.

* 'London' can be replaced by any other relevant place name.

Teacher's Notes

- This is a good song for music and movement. What other words can the children think of to replace 'running', e.g. marching, stamping, hopping?
- Do any of the children have relatives or friends who have run a marathon? What type of preparation do they think is involved? What sort of person might take on such a challenge? Can they think of other situations that may require such dedication and determination? Have they ever been determined to achieve something, and practised it until they could do it (such as whistling, hopping, skipping, playing a musical instrument)?

(May Day: 1 May)

1 Dance, dance round and round,
Let your feet skip over the ground.
Dancing round the maypole on the first of May.

2 Hold your ribbon high,
Hold it up to the sky.
Dancing round the maypole on the first of May.

3 Weaving in and out,
Reaching up, ducking down.
Dancing round the maypole on the first of May.

4 Repeat verse 1

Teacher's Notes

- Make a ribbon picture. Gather together a few strands of differently coloured ribbon and stick the tops of the ribbon together at the top of a piece of paper. Have fun making patterns with the dangling ribbons.
- Maypole dancing is a type of folk dance. Can the children think of any others?

FRIEND TO THE WORLD

(World Environment Day: 5 June)

1 Oh, we've got a wonderful world,
Oh, we've got a wonderful world.
So, let's be clever, we can all work together,
Be a friend, friend to the world.

2 We can all look after our world,
We can all look after our world.
So, let's be clever, we can all work together,
Be a friend, friend to the world.

3 It's the most incredible world,
It's the most incredible world.
So, let's be clever, we can all work together,
Be a friend, friend to the world.

4 Repeat verse 1

Teacher's Notes

- What is it that makes our planet unique? Talk about the fact that we have the sun, moon, water and air – all of which help our planet to sustain life.
- What sorts of things have the children heard about that help us look after our world? (Recycling, lack of pollution (e.g. not dropping litter), conserving energy, caring for wildlife, etc.)
- Ask the children to make a note of how many times they do the following things during a period of 24 hours: turn on a tap, turn on a light, watch the TV, use a computer, etc. Make a graph of your findings.
- A wildlife garden is a great way to attract nature into your nursery/school grounds. If you already have one, take the children to look around it and discuss the different wildlife that live there. Talk about how the destruction of woodland, pollution of rivers and ponds, and the use of pesticides and herbicides have each contributed to the reduced amount of wildlife in Britain and why it's important to help our wildlife thrive.

IT'S AN EASY THING TO DO

(Recycle Now Week: c. 20–26 June)

1 Have you got some cardboard you want to throw away?
Put it in the bin, put it in the bin,
Put it in the bin with the cardboard in.
It's an easy thing to do,
I recycle, so can you.

2 Have you got some paper you want to throw away?
Put it in the bin, put it in the bin,
Put it in the bin with the paper in.
It's an easy thing to do,
I recycle, so can you.

3 Have you got some plastic you want to throw away?
Put it in the bin, put it in the bin,
Put it in the bin with the plastic in.
It's an easy thing to do,
I recycle, so can you.

4 Have you got a bottle you want to throw away?
Put it in the bin, put it in the bin,
Put it in the bin with the bottles in.
It's an easy thing to do,
I recycle, so can you.

5 Have you got a tin can you want to throw away?
Put it in the bin, put it in the bin,
Put it in the bin with the tin cans in.
It's an easy thing to do,
I recycle, so can you.
It's an easy thing to do,
I recycle, so can you.

Teacher's Notes

The children will have to work hard to get their tongues around some of the lyrics in this song! Try some warm-up vocal exercises before you begin. Using the first five notes of a scale, go up and down using the following words repeatedly: Harry Potter; poppa kettle; shiny shoeshine. You can vary the pitch you begin on to add variety to the exercise. Once you've done this a few times, take the words 'put it in the bin' from the song and repeat these on a single note. Work your way up the scale. Now your tongues should be well and truly warmed up, so enjoy singing the song!

IT'S FATHER'S DAY

(June)

1 Give him a cheer, give him a cheer,
Because to me it's very clear
That Dad deserves a special day,
So give him a cheer, it's Father's Day.

2 Give him a hug, give him a hug,
Make him tea in his favourite mug,
'Cos Dad deserves a special day
So give him a hug, it's Father's Day.

3 Give him a smile, give him a smile,
Tell him to have some fun for a while,
'Cos Dad deserves a special day
So give him a smile, it's Father's Day.

4 Repeat verse 1

Teacher's Notes

- Can the children name funny things that dads do that make the children laugh?
- What small things could the children do for their dads on Father's Day to make them smile?

Are You Ready for Some Summer Fun?

(Summer)

1 The sun is shining, shining down,
Shining down, shining down.
The sun is shining, shining down,
Are you ready for some summer fun?

2 The birds are flying in the sky,
In the sky, in the sky.
The birds are flying in the sky,
Are you ready for some summer fun?

3 The flowers are blooming everywhere,
Everywhere, everywhere.
The flowers are blooming everywhere,
Are you ready for some summer fun?

4 The barbecue is getting hot,
Getting hot, getting hot.
The barbecue is getting hot,
Are you ready for some summer fun?

5 Repeat verse 1

Teacher's Notes

- Have a go at adding some verses to this song. Look at the number of syllables in the first line of lyrics (8). You'll see that this is split into two sections – the first taking five syllables and the last, three. This is important to note when you're constructing your own phrases as you'll need to repeat the last section in the second line, so it must make sense on its own. See if the children can make up some phrases that will fit and enjoy singing your new song.
- Make a list of all the things that the children associate with summer and have fun making a big collage including them all.

(International Literacy Day: 8 September)

1 There's a space machine in my book,
Would you like to take a look?
There's a world of fun in my book,
Come and read the story of the space machine.

2 There's a magic key in my book,
Would you like to take a look?
There's a world of fun in my book,
Come and read the story of the magic key.

3 There's a cheeky gnome in my book,
Would you like to take a look?
There's a world of fun in my book,
Come and read the story of the cheeky gnome.

4 There's a friendly bear in my book,
Would you like to take a look?
There's a world of fun in my book,
Come and read the story of the friendly bear

5 There's a pirate ship in my book,
Would you like to take a look?
There's a world of fun in my book,
Come and read the story of the pirate ship.

Teacher's Notes

Listen through to this song with the children (CD track 14). Can they hear the different accompaniment that the arranger has given each verse? He's done this to help describe the lyrics through the music. Split the class into five groups and allocate a different verse to each one. Produce a selection of different percussion instruments and see if they can choose some to play along to their verse, complimenting each subject. They could even sing their verse differently to suit, for example using robotic sounding voices for verse 2 or a pirate's 'ooh-aargh-me-hearties' voice for verse 5.

THANK YOU FOR THE HARVEST

(September/October)

1 Leeks and beans and cauliflowers,
Ready for the harvest time.
Leeks and beans and cauliflowers,
Ripe and plump and fine.

CHORUS So thank you, thank you,
Thank you for the harvest.
Thank you, thank you,
For the harvest time.

2 Pears and plums and strawberries,
Ready for the harvest time.
Pears and plums and strawberries,
Ripe and plump and fine.

CHORUS

3 Wheat and oats and yellow corn,
Ready for the harvest time.
Wheat and oats and yellow corn,
Ripe and plump and fine.

CHORUS

4 Carrots, peas and cabbages,
Ready for the harvest time.
Carrots, peas and cabbages,
Ripe and plump and fine.

CHORUS x 2

Teacher's Notes

Talk about how each food mentioned in the song grows. Which ones grow underground; which grow up from the ground; which grow on trees; and which grow in fields?

Crunching Through the Leaves

(Autumn)

1 Crunching through the leaves, crunching, crunching,
Crunching through the leaves, listen to the sound.
Crunching through the leaves, crunching, crunching,
Watch them falling, falling down.

2 Floating in the breeze, floating, floating,
Floating in the breeze, red and gold and brown.
Floating in the breeze, floating, floating,
Watch them falling, falling down.

3 Spinning in the sun, spinning, spinning,
Spinning in the sun, turning all around.
Spinning in the sun, spinning, spinning,
Watch them falling, falling down.

4 Repeat verse 1

Teacher's Notes

- This is an excellent song for adding untuned percussion to. Look/listen to each verse and decide together which sounds could best represent the actions of the leaves. You could even gather together some dry, crunchy leaves in a box and shake it – perfect for verses 1 and 4!
- Have fun making an autumn patchwork picture. Take the children out to collect leaves, acorns, conkers, etc. Cut out lots of brightly coloured squares of paper and give one to each child to decorate.

WEAR A POPPY TODAY

(Remembrance Day: 11 November)

1 Brave men and women fought to keep us safe,
Fought to keep us safe, fought to keep us safe.
Brave men and women fought to keep us safe,
So wear a poppy today.

2 Always remember, never to forget,
Never to forget, never to forget.
Always remember, never to forget,
So wear a poppy today.

3 They did their duty so we could live in peace,
We could live in peace, we could live in peace.
They did their duty so we could live in peace,
So wear a poppy today.

4 Brave men and women fought to keep us safe,
Fought to keep us safe, fought to keep us safe.
Brave men and women fought to keep us safe,
So wear a poppy today,
So wear a poppy today.

Teacher's Notes

- For most children, the concept of Remembrance Day is a difficult one to comprehend. The simplicity of the lyrics in this song help them to begin to understand why we spend a period of time each year remembering those who fought and gave their lives for our country.
- On Remembrance Day, a period of silence is usually observed at 11am. Silence is a rare thing in today's world of traffic, mobile phones, TV, radio, sirens... and even in the depths of the countryside, it is rare to hear no sound at all. Ask the children to sit still and silently on the floor and close their eyes. How many sounds can they hear in just one minute?
- Find out why we use poppies as a symbol for Remembrance Day. It's a perfect flower to draw, and you can make great pictures or wreaths to display at this time of year.

Give a Little Smile

(World Kindness Day: 13 November
Anti-bullying Week: c. 14–18 November)

1 Give a little smile,
Give a little smile
And be kind to everyone.
It doesn't cost a thing,
It's easy just to bring
A little smile to everyone.

2 Bring a little love,
Bring a little love
And be good to everyone.
It doesn't cost a thing,
It's easy just to bring
A little love to everyone.

3 Give a little help,
Give a little help
And be nice to everyone.
It doesn't cost a thing,
It's easy just to bring
A little help to everyone.

4 Repeat verse 1

Teacher's Notes

- Can the children think of something kind that they have done, or somebody has done for them in the last few days? How does it make them feel when somebody smiles at them? Talk about how offering kindness to somebody is easy to do, and doesn't cost a thing, but it can make a difference to someone's day.
- Ask the children to make the effort to smile at at least five people during the day. Afterwards, discuss how this made them feel. Perhaps you could have a 'smilathon' or even a 'hugathon' and raise some money for a good cause by smiling at/hugging a certain number of people in one day.

Behind the Window

(Advent: December)

1 Will there be a robin, a little robin bobbin,
Behind the window, behind the window?
Will there be a robin, a little robin bobbin,
Behind my advent calendar window?

2 Will there be some star shine, some spingle, spangle star shine,
Behind the window, behind the window?
Will there be some star shine, some spingle, spangle star shine,
Behind my advent calendar window?

3 Will there be a camel, a lumpy, bumpy camel,
Behind the window, behind the window?
Will there be a camel, a lumpy, bumpy camel,
Behind my advent calendar window?

4 Will there be a Santa, a jolly, jolly Santa,
Behind the window, behind the window?
Will there be a Santa, a jolly, jolly Santa,
Behind my advent calendar window?

5 Will there be a baby, a precious little baby,
Behind the window, behind the window?
Will there be a baby, a precious little baby,
Behind my advent calendar window?

Teacher's Notes

Have some fun making advent calendars. You can do this either by drawing your own pictures to reveal or by cutting some out of magazines. Start with two pieces of the same-size paper (or thin card). On your first piece of paper, draw a Christmassy scene that will be the front of your advent calendar. Enjoy decorating this with lots of glitter, and mark out squares for the calendar windows. Number these from 1 to 24. The children will need some help cutting out three sides of each square to form the windows.

Lay the Christmas scene over the second sheet of paper (it helps to hold this in place at the corners with sticky tack) and carefully open each window to mark where it will appear on the bottom sheet. Remove the top sheet and stick your reveal pictures where you have marked. Glue around the edges of the bottom sheet and stick the top sheet over it, ensuring all the windows are closed ready for 1 December.

HAPPY CHRISTMAS!

(December)

1 Have you hung your stocking up?
There's not much time to go.
Santa will be on his way
With a smile and a ho, ho, ho.

CHORUS Happy Christmas,
Happy Christmas,
Happy Christmas to everyone today.

2 Have you made a Christmas cake
With icing on the top?
And a sticky Christmas pud?
It's lovely nice and hot.

CHORUS

3 Have you seen the pretty lights
That sparkle in the street?
Will you dream of them tonight
When you go to sleep?

CHORUS

4 Have you wrapped some presents up
And made them nice and bright?
Are you going to put them
Underneath the tree tonight?

CHORUS x 2

Teacher's Notes

The song describes some of the traditions we celebrate at Christmas time, but there are lots of other ways people celebrate around the world. Can the children find out about any of these? Have a look at Poland, Australia, America and Africa and see if they do anything differently.

It's a New Year

(January)

Words and Music by
Niki Davies

1. 2. 3.
F Gm11 B♭add9 Fmaj7 Gm11 F6 Dm7 G7 B♭add9/C C7
you.
you.
you.
2. It's
4.
F Gm11 Gm9/C C7 C6 F6/C Gm9 B♭ B♭/C C7
you. So wel - come, wel - come, wel - come to
F B♭6 B♭/D F B♭ B♭/C F C7 F F/C F
you.
3 3 3

DRAGON DANCE

(Chinese New Year: January/February)

Words and Music by
Niki Davies

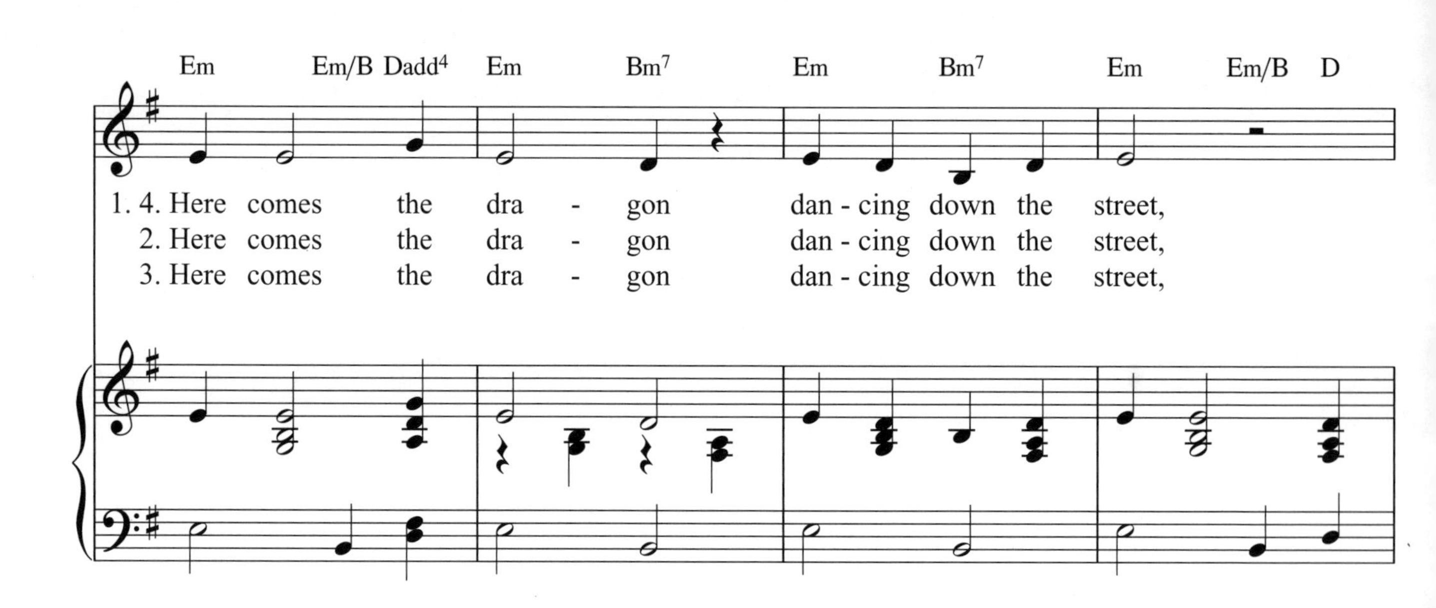

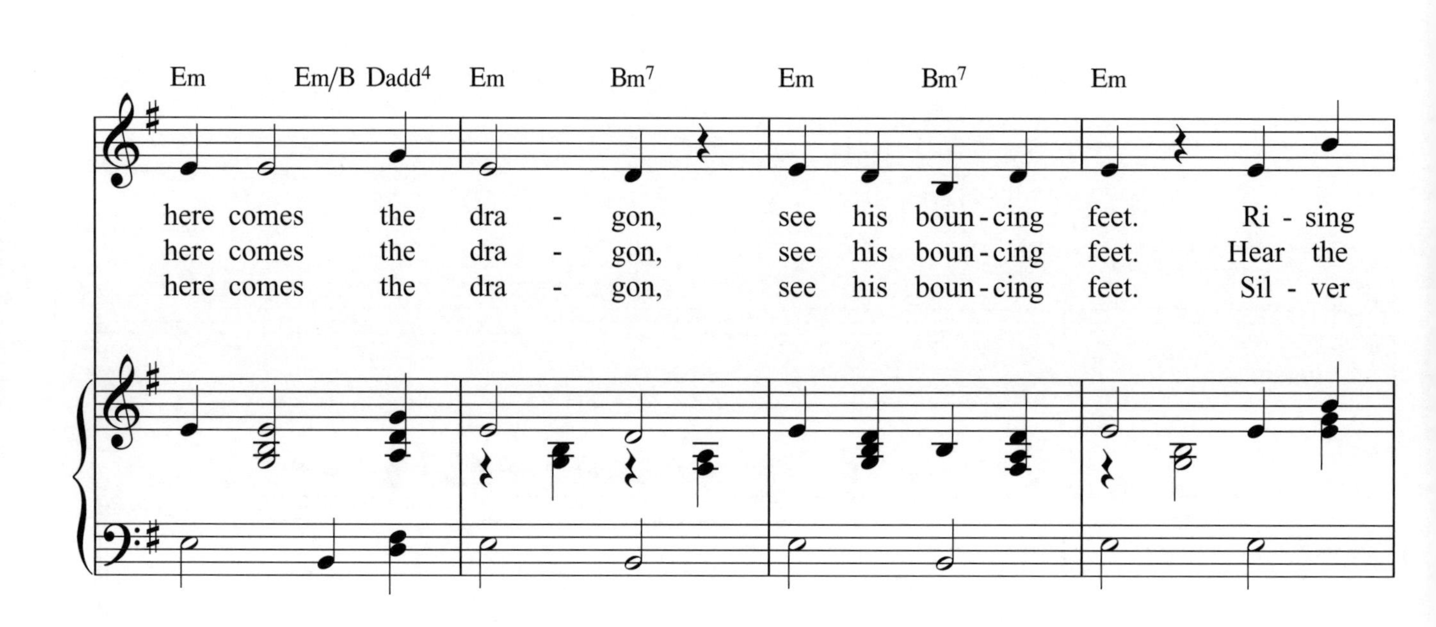

Am Aadd2sus4 Am A13sus4 Em Dadd4/B Em Am Aadd2sus4
up to the sky, swoop-ing down from on high, see him leap, see him
sound of the gong as he dan - ces a - long, see him leap, see him
scales bright as day, and the drum beats a - way, see him leap, see him
1. 2. 3.
4.
Am Em Dadd4/B Em Em
prance, do - ing the dra - gon dance. dance.
prance, do - ing the dra - gon dance.
prance, do - ing the dra - gon dance.

N.C.

VALENTINE

(14 February)

Words and Music by
Niki Davies

Smoothly ♩ = 124

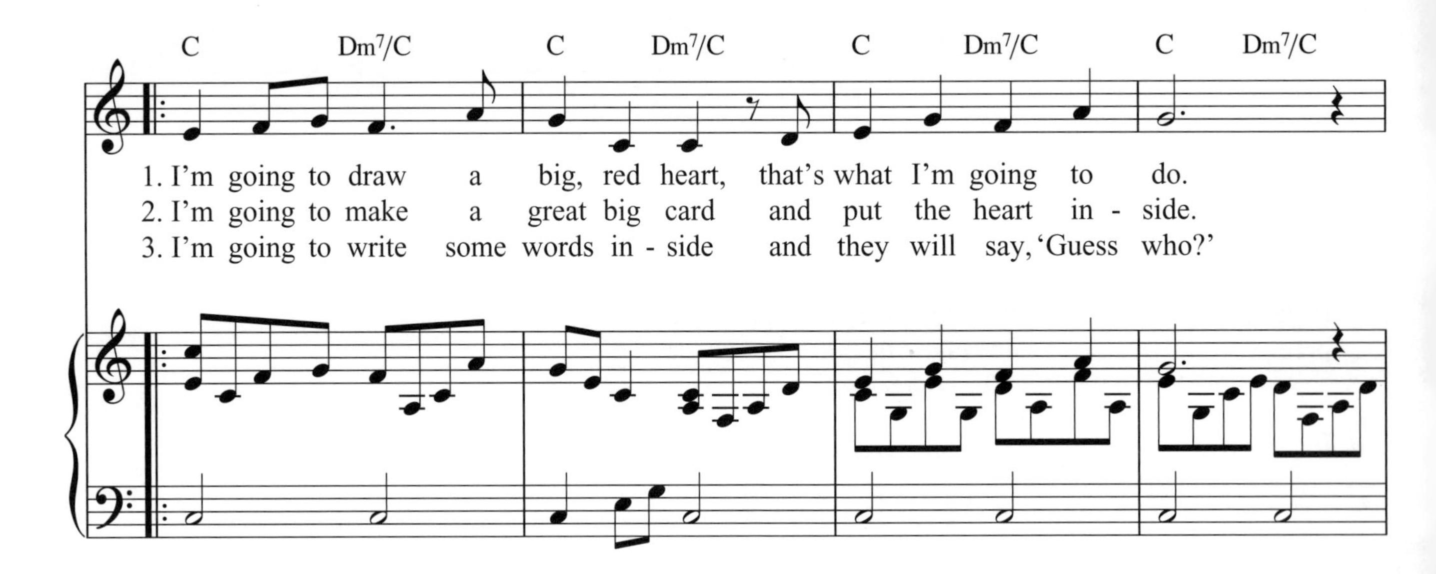

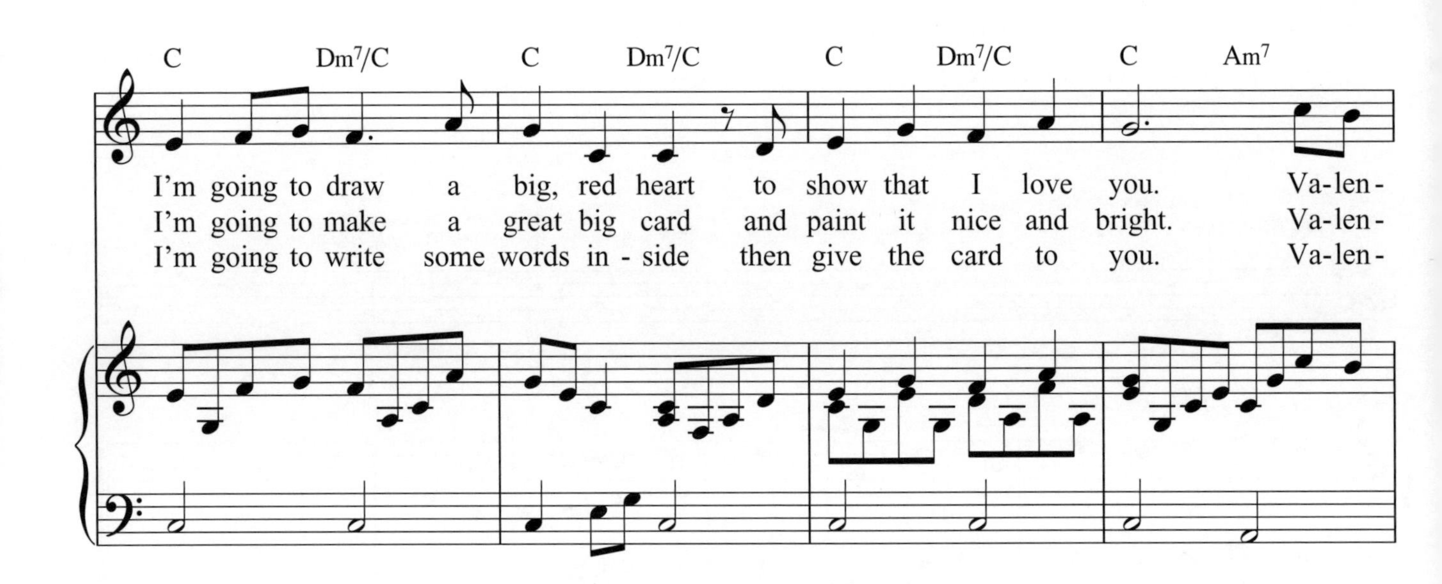

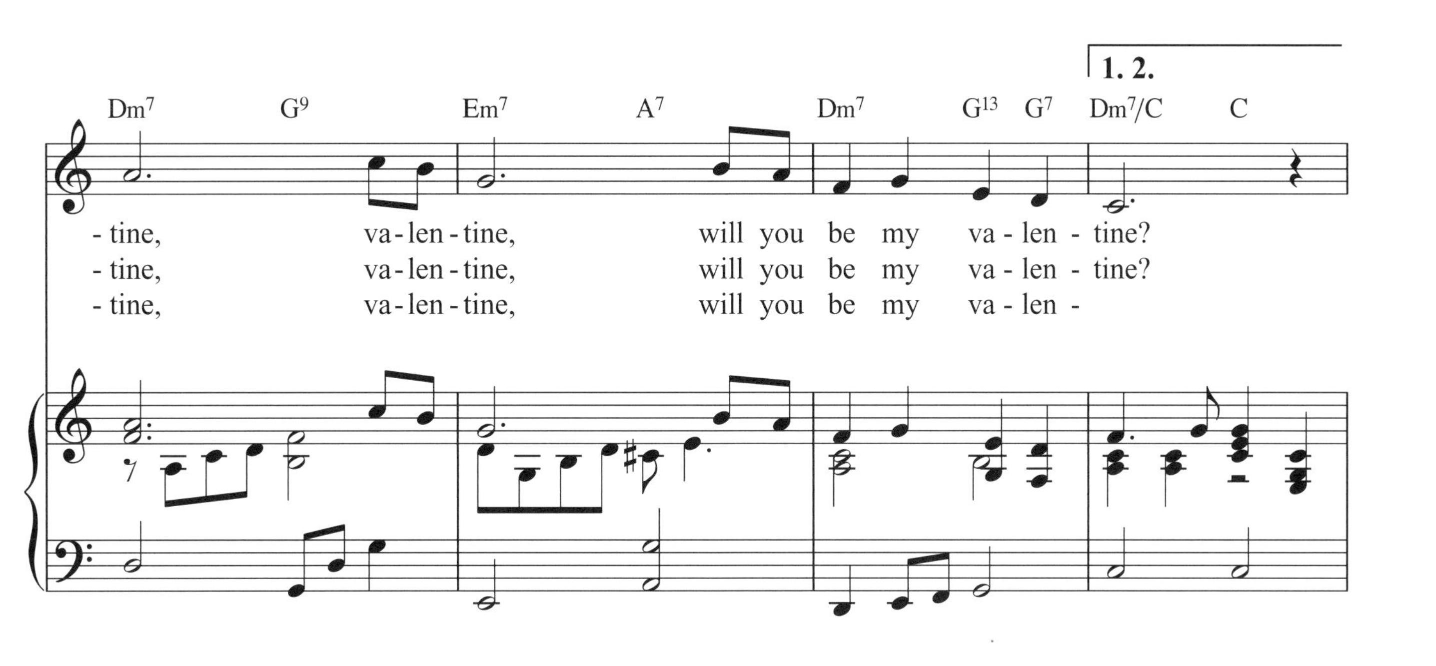
1. 2.
Dm7
G9
Em7
A7
Dm7
G13
G7
Dm7/C
C
- tine, va - len - tine, will you be my va - len - tine?
- tine, va - len - tine, will you be my va - len - tine?
- tine, va - len - tine, will you be my va - len -

3.
Dm7/C
Cmaj7
Dm7/C
C
Dm7
Gsus4
G
Dm7/C
C
- tine?

rit.
Dm7/C
Cmaj7
Dm7/C
G11
C
Dm7/C
C
G9
G7
C

There's a Pancake on the Ceiling!

(Shrove Tuesday: February/March)

Words and Music by
Niki Davies

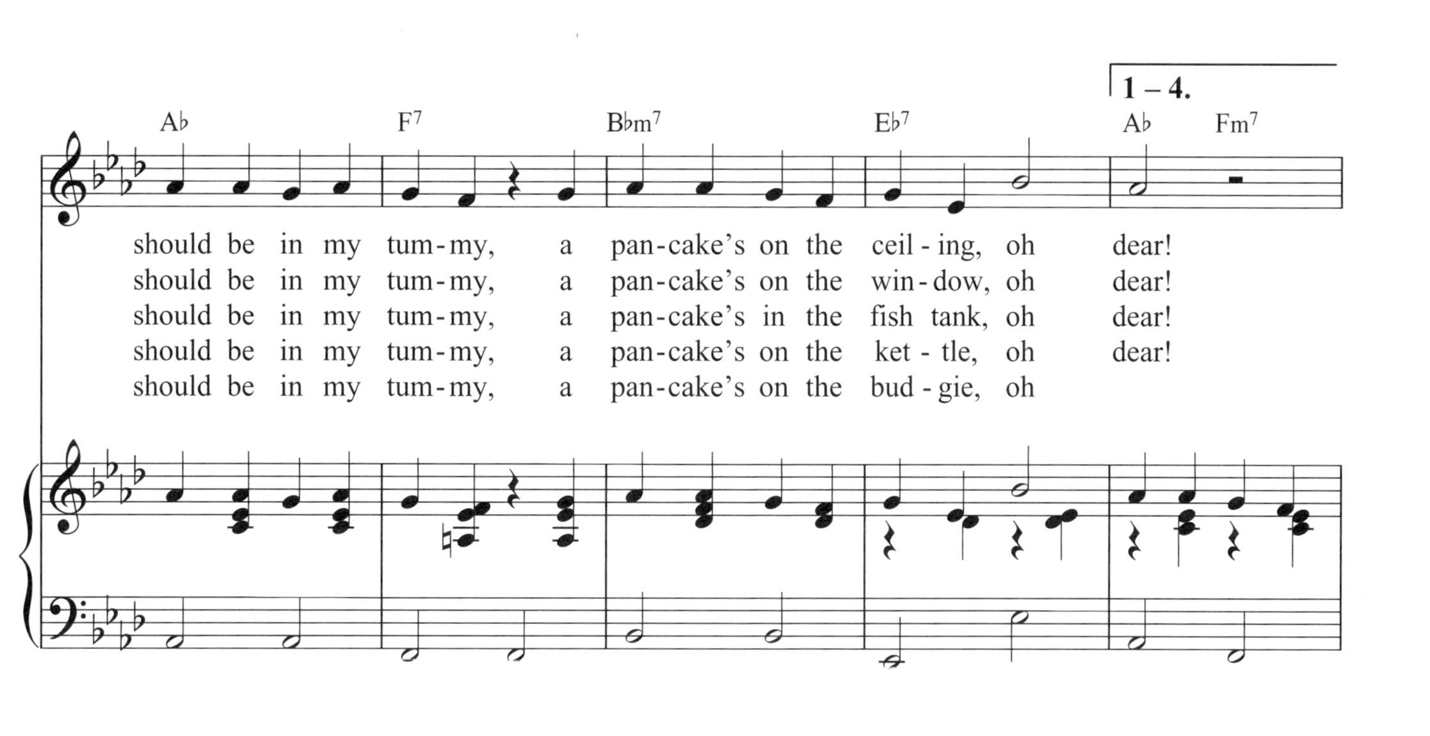
1 – 4.
A♭
F7
B♭m7
E♭7
A♭
Fm7
should be in my tum-my, a pan-cake's on the ceil-ing, oh dear!
should be in my tum-my, a pan-cake's on the win-dow, oh dear!
should be in my tum-my, a pan-cake's in the fish tank, oh dear!
should be in my tum-my, a pan-cake's on the ket-tle, oh dear!
should be in my tum-my, a pan-cake's on the bud-gie, oh

5.
E♭7
A♭
Fm7
B♭m11
E♭7
A♭
Fm7
2. There's a
dear!
3. There's a
4. There's a
5. There's a

E♭7
A♭
Fm7
B♭m11
E♭7
A♭
E♭7
A♭

CAN YOU THINK OF A WORD?

(World Poetry Day: 21 March)

Words and Music by
Niki Davies

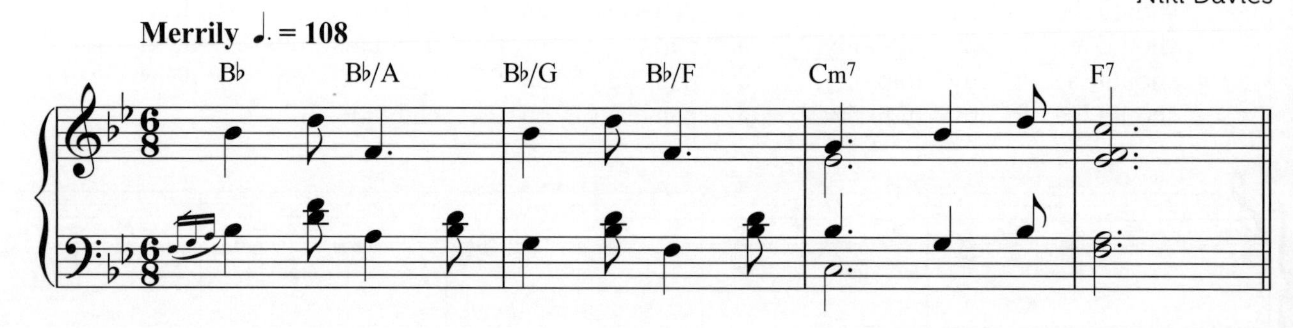

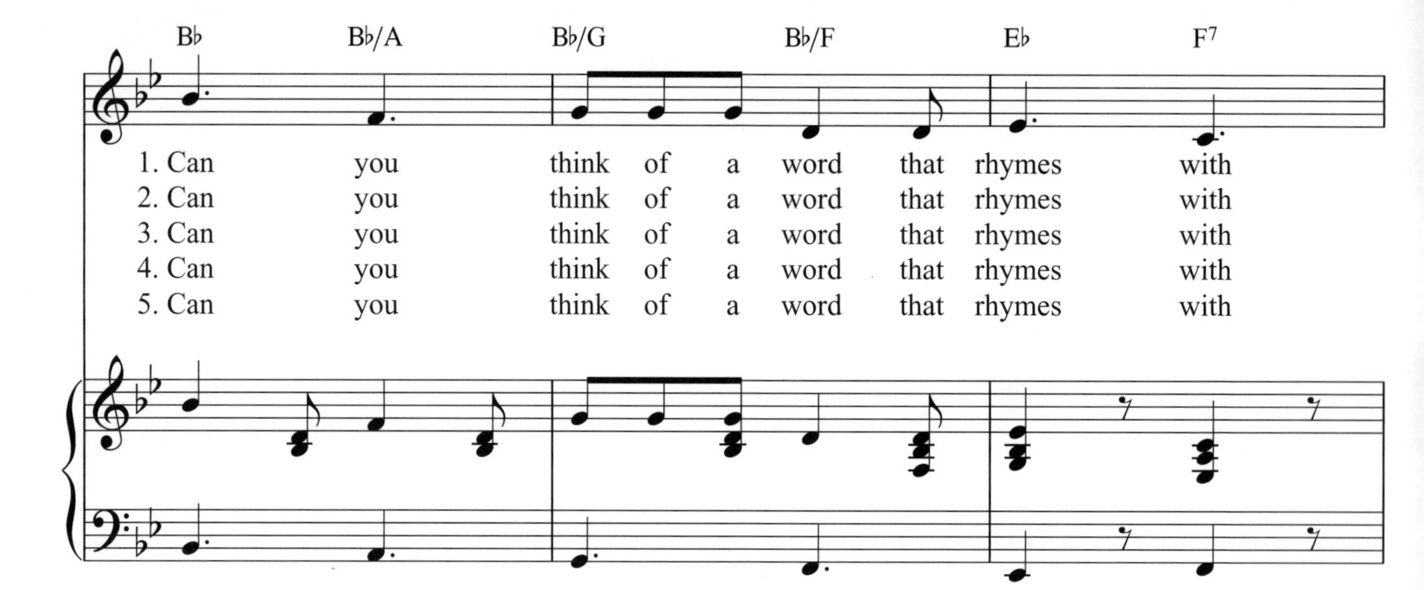

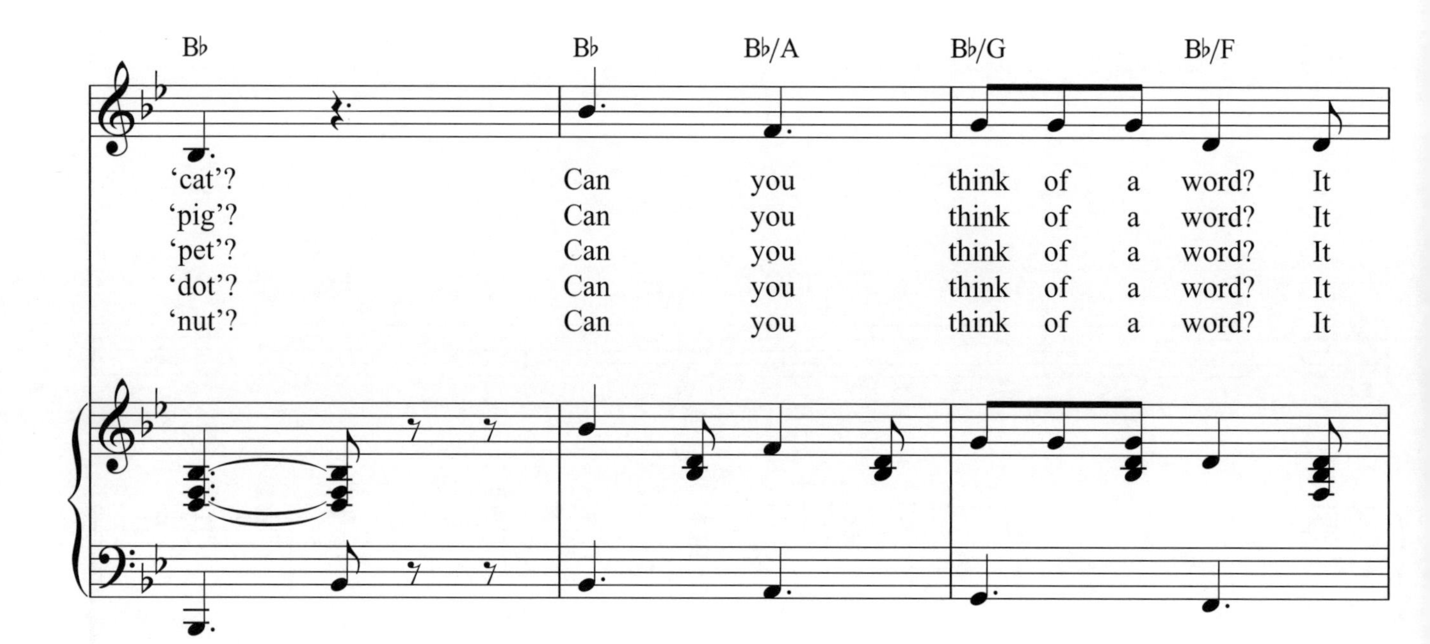

Cm/E♭ Cm7 F Cm7 F
could be 'mat'. I think a good one
could be 'fig'. I think a good one
could be 'vet'. I think a good one
could be 'pot'. I think a good one
could be 'hut'. I think a good one
D7 Gm E♭ F
would be 'bat' be-cause it rhymes with
would be 'dig' be-cause it rhymes with
would be 'wet' be-cause it rhymes with
would be 'lot' be-cause it rhymes with
would be 'but' be-cause it rhymes with
1 – 4.
5.
B♭ F7 B♭ B♭ F7 B♭
'cat'.
'pig'.
'pet'.
'dot'.
'nut'.

Have a Day Off, Mum

(Mother's Day: March/April)

Words and Music by
Niki Davies

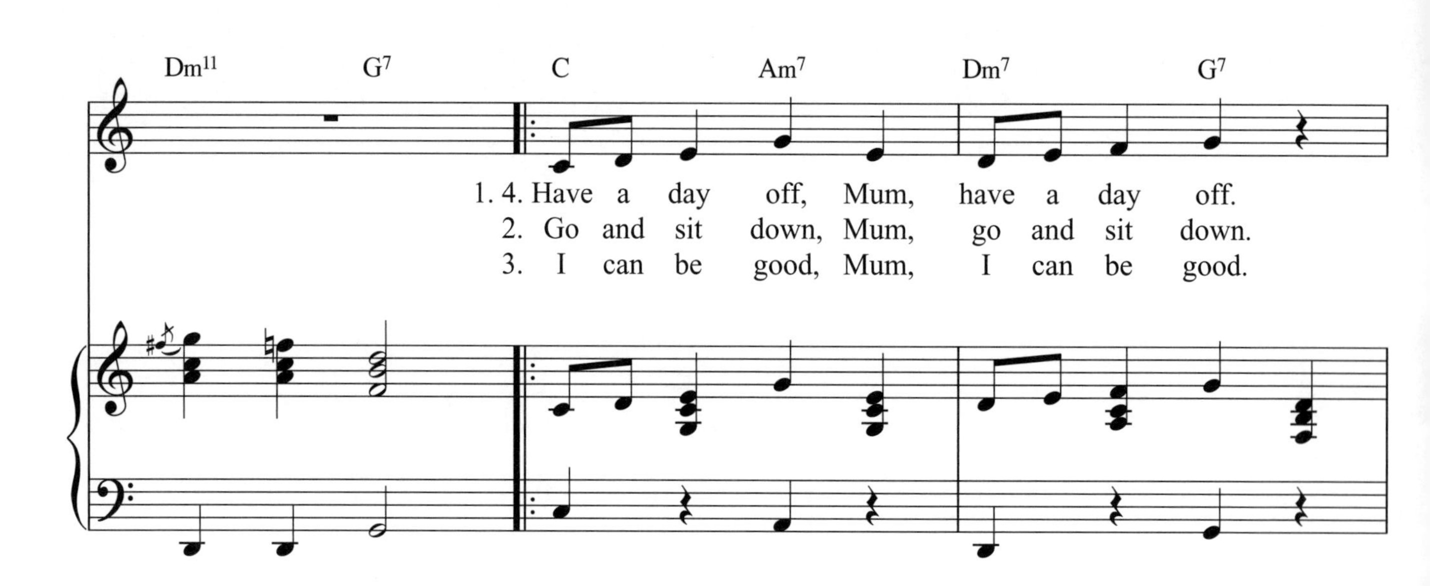

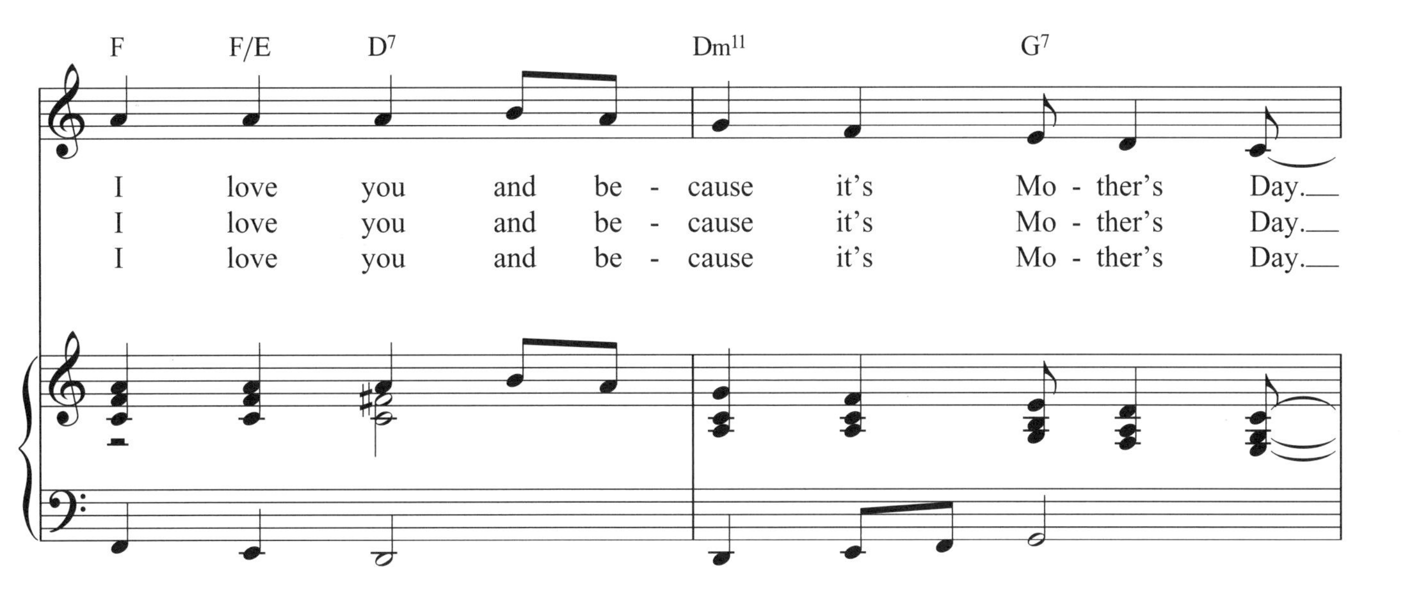
F F/E D7 Dm11 G7
I love you and be - cause it's Mo - ther's Day.
I love you and be - cause it's Mo - ther's Day.
I love you and be - cause it's Mo - ther's Day.

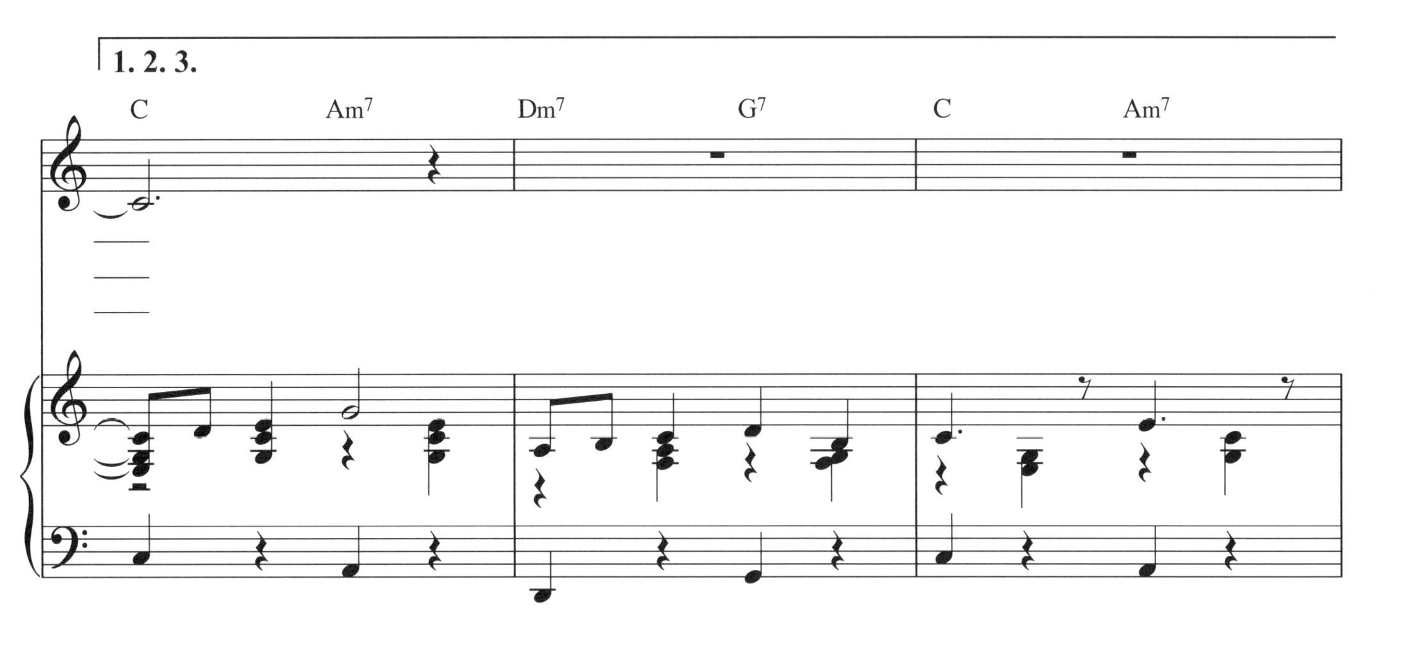
1. 2. 3.
C Am7 Dm7 G7 C Am7

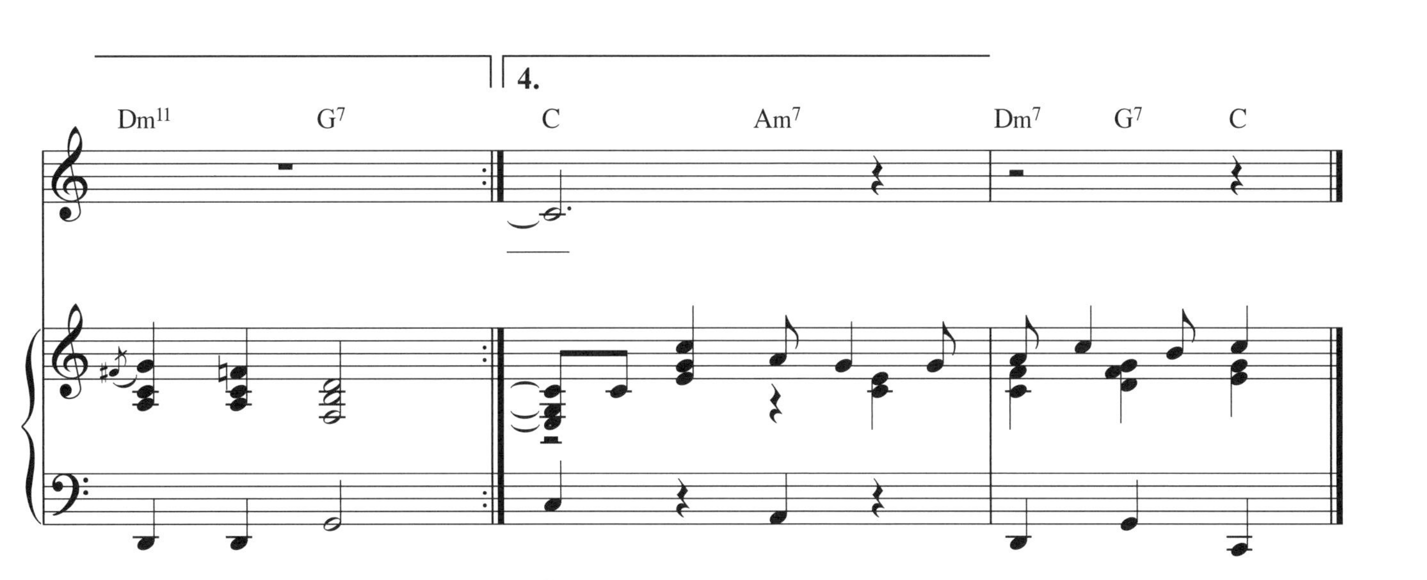
4.
Dm11 G7 C Am7 Dm7 G7 C

There's a Bear in the Fridge

(April Fool's Day: 1 April)

Words and Music by
Niki Davies

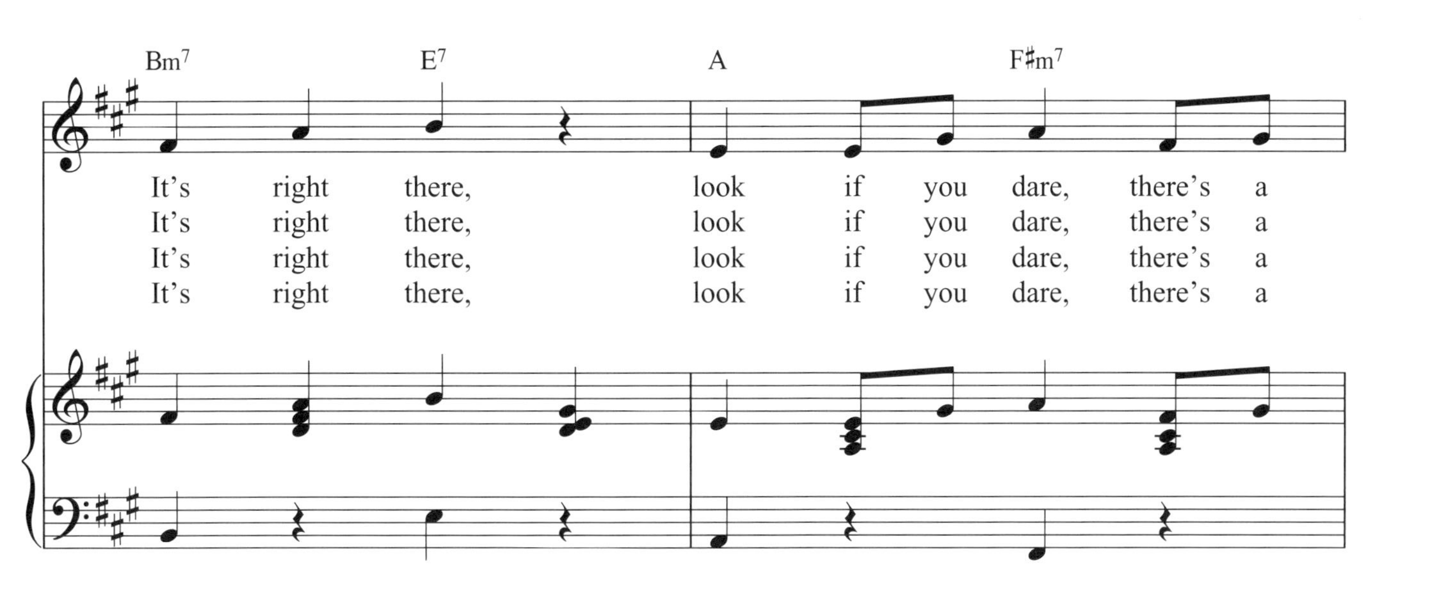
Bm7
E7
A
F♯m7
It's right there, look if you dare, there's a
It's right there, look if you dare, there's a
It's right there, look if you dare, there's a
It's right there, look if you dare, there's a

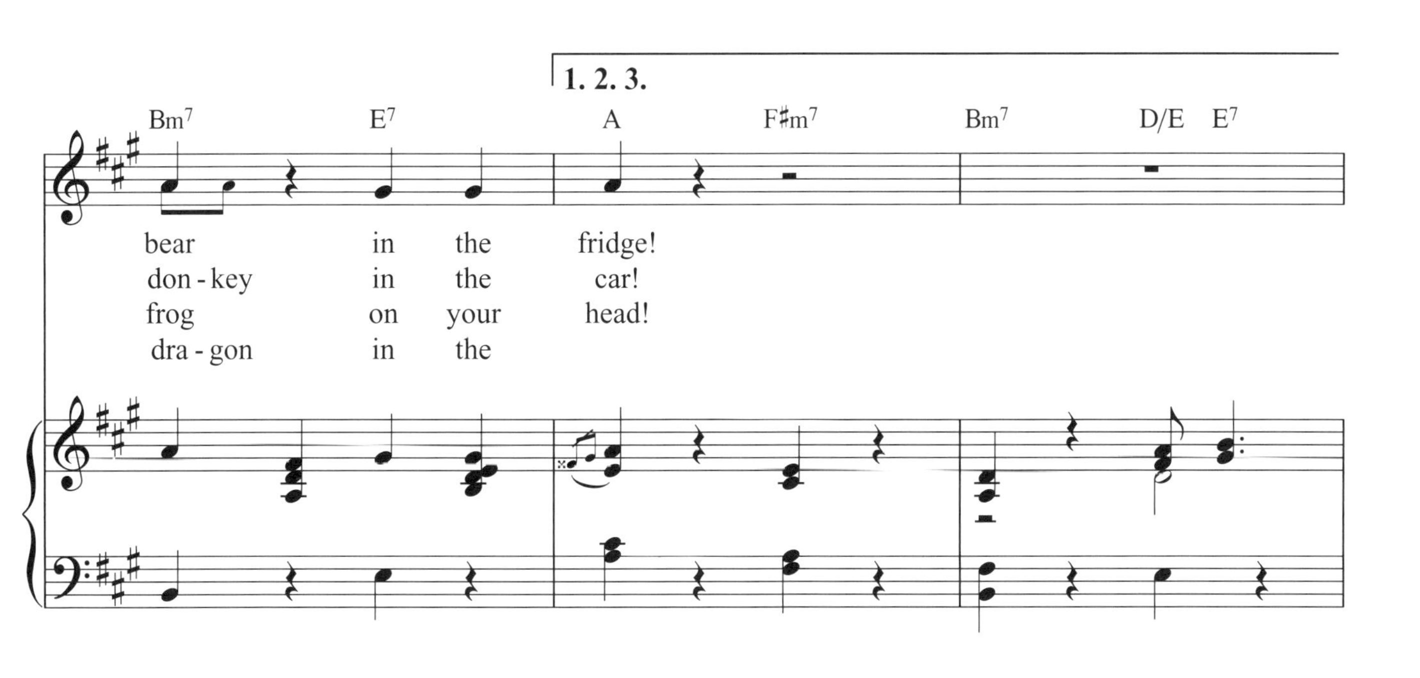
1. 2. 3.
Bm7
E7
A
F♯m7
Bm7
D/E
E7
bear in the fridge!
don-key in the car!
frog on your head!
dra-gon in the

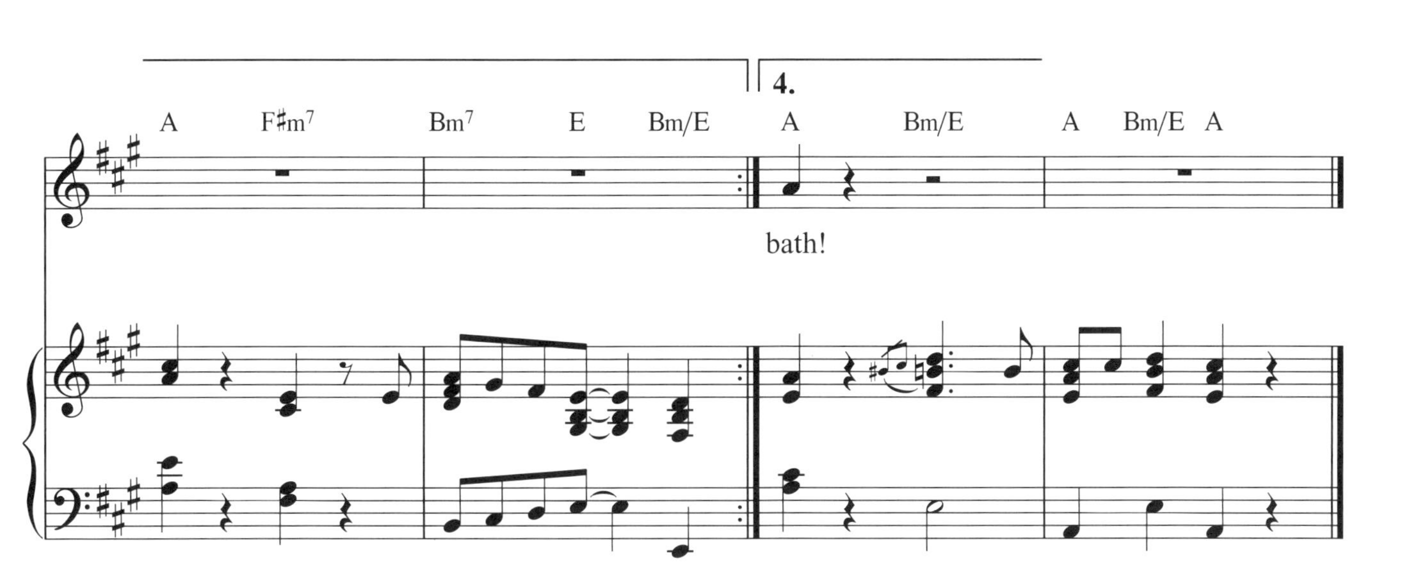
4.
A
F♯m7
Bm7
E
Bm/E
A
Bm/E
A
Bm/E
A
bath!

It's the London Marathon

(April)

Words and Music by
Niki Davies

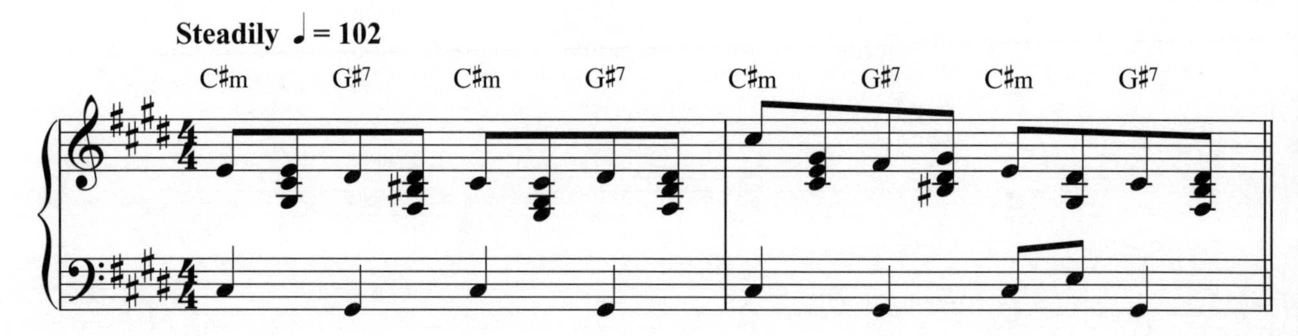

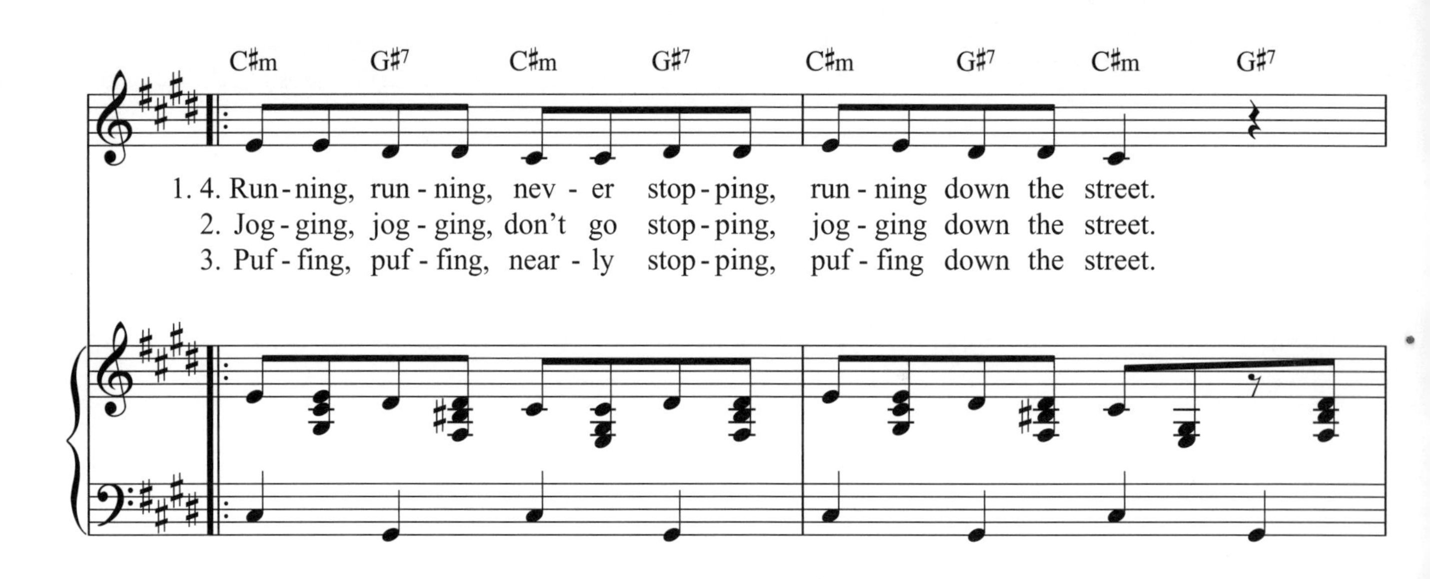

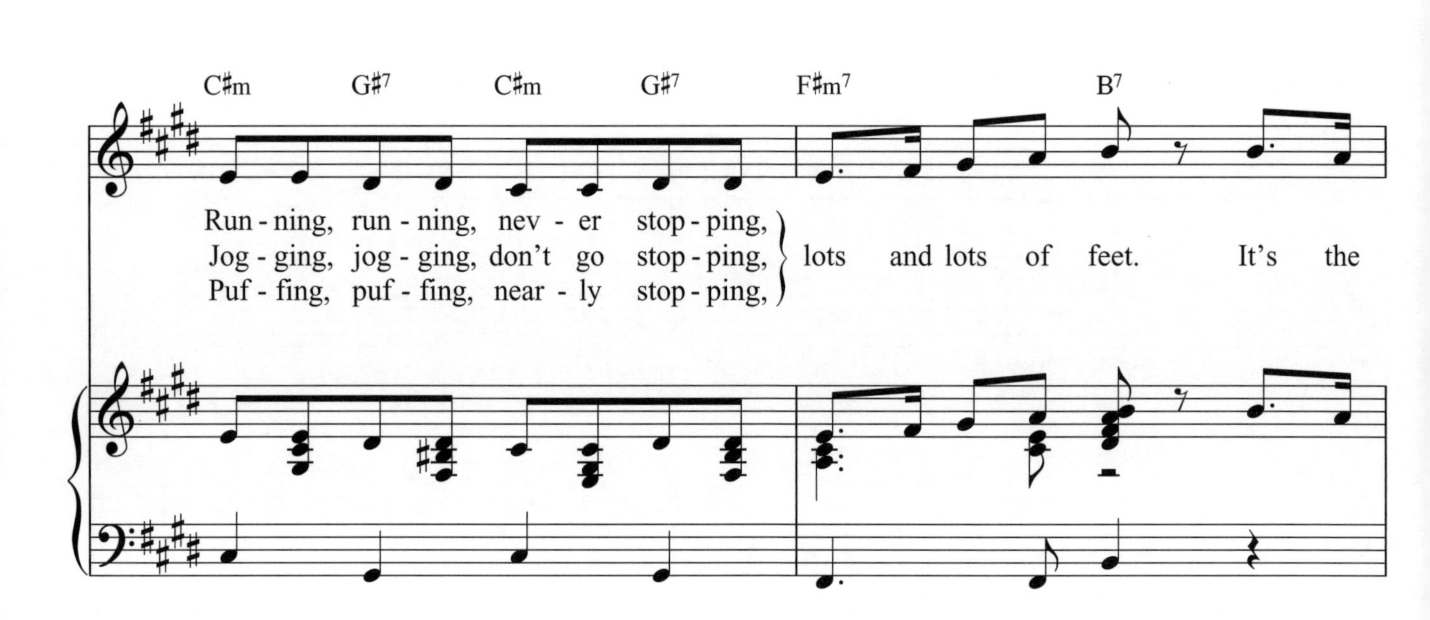

* 'London' can be replaced by any other relevant place name.

MAYPOLE

(May Day: 1 May)

Words and Music by
Niki Davies

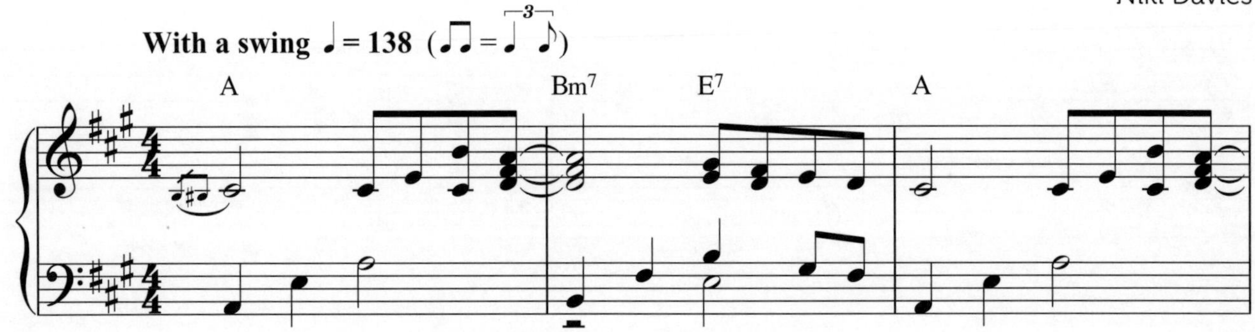

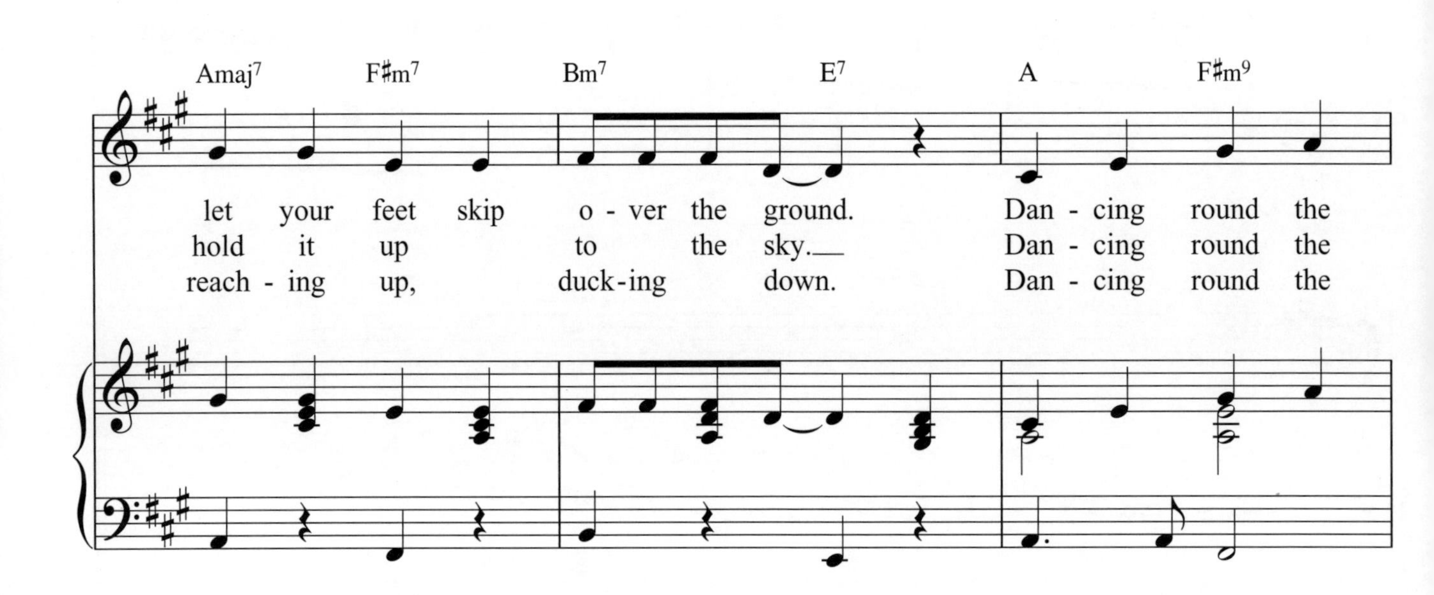

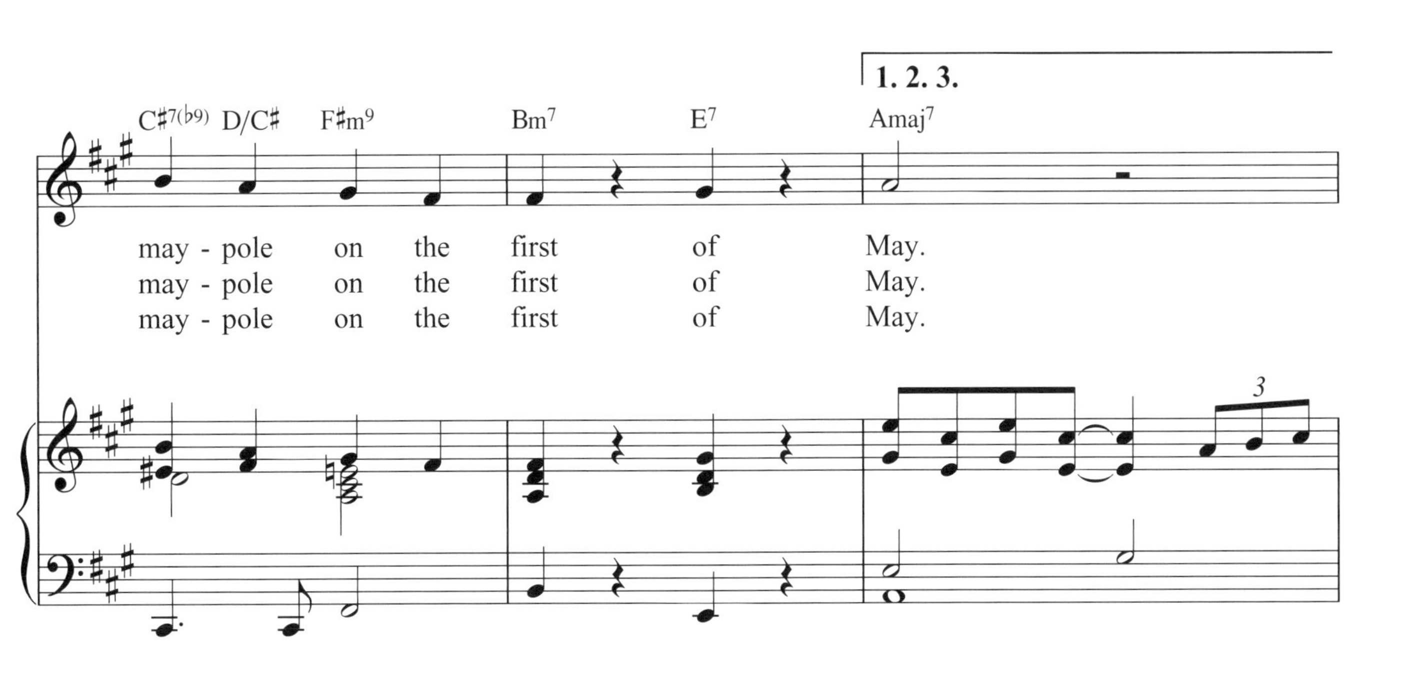
1. 2. 3.
C♯7(♭9) D/C♯ F♯m9 Bm7 E7 Amaj7
may - pole on the first of May.
may - pole on the first of May.
may - pole on the first of May.
3

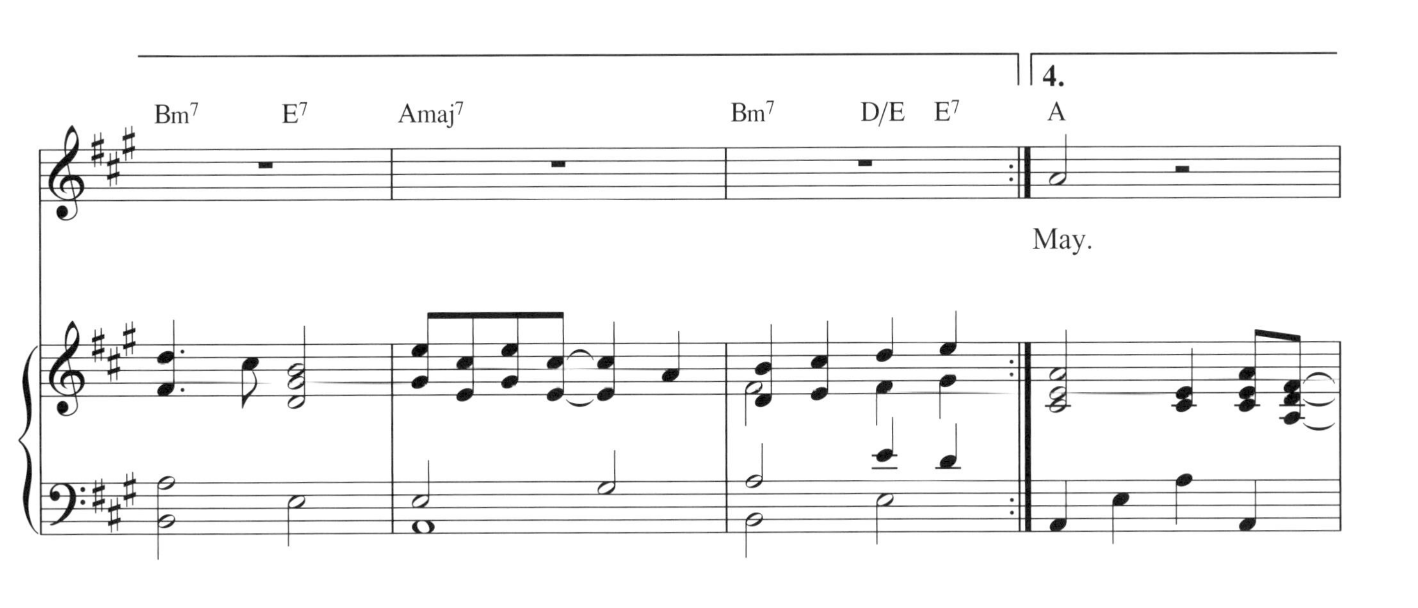
4.
Bm7 E7 Amaj7 Bm7 D/E E7 A
May.

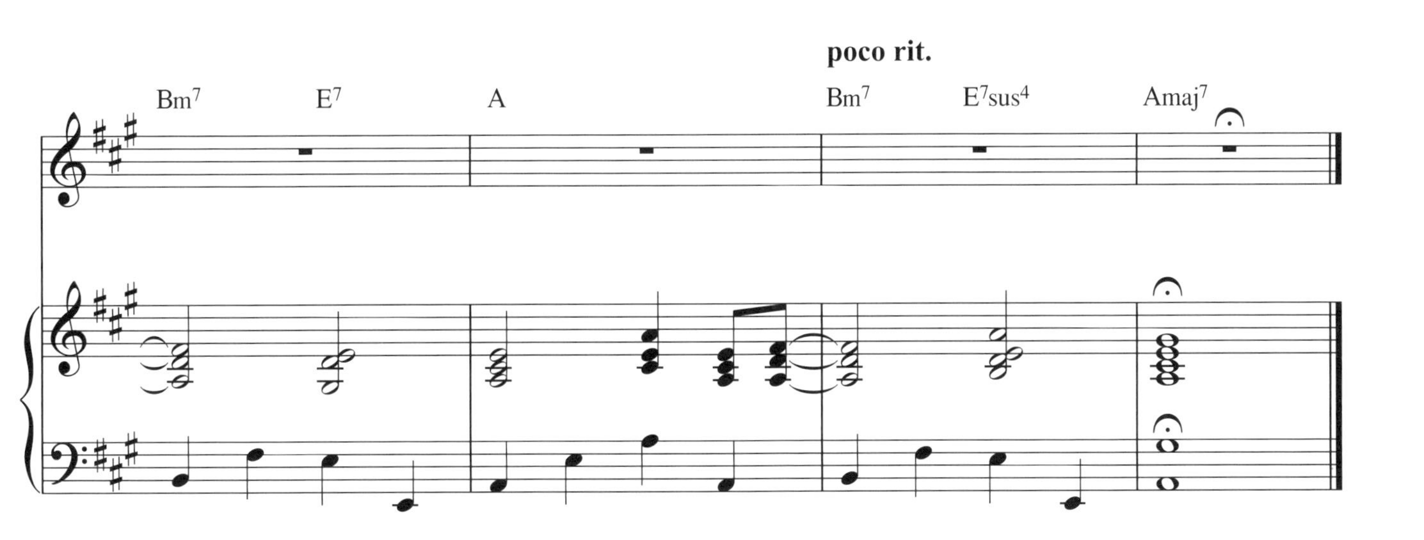
poco rit.
Bm7 E7 A Bm7 E7sus4 Amaj7

FRIEND TO THE WORLD

(World Environment Day: 5 June)

Words and Music by
Niki Davies

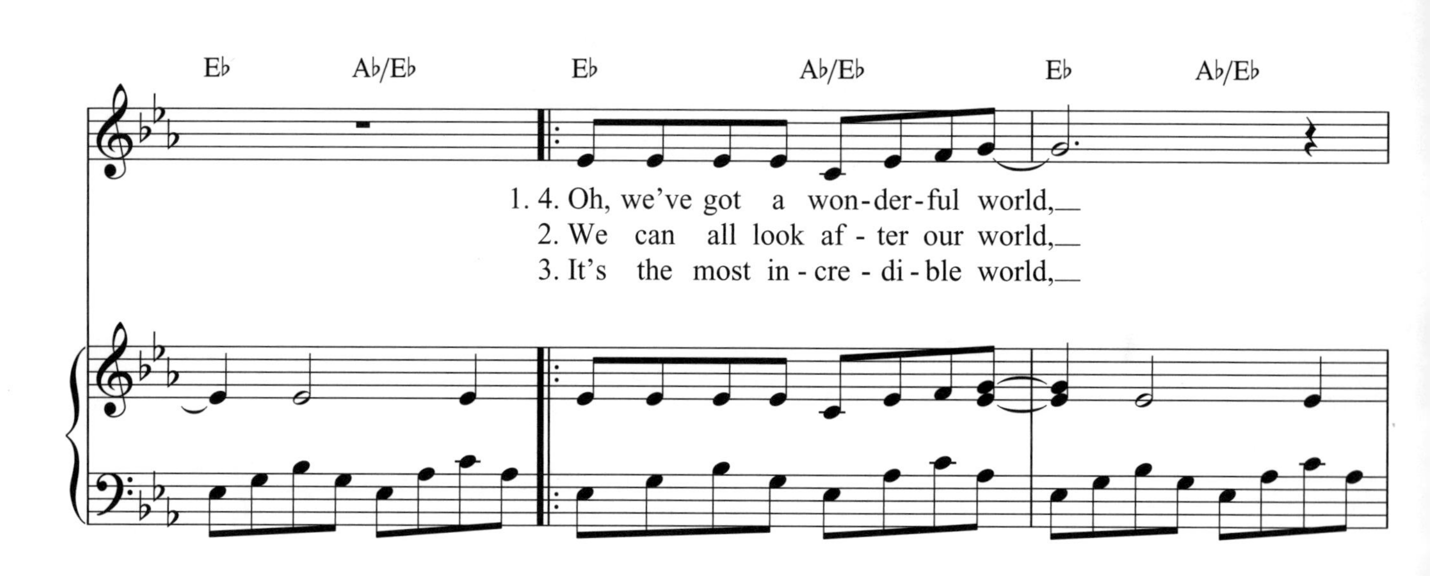

E♭maj7/B♭
Fm11/B♭
1. 2. 3.
all work to-ge-ther, be a friend,
friend to the world.
E♭
A♭/E♭
E♭
A♭/B♭
E♭
A♭/E♭
E♭
A♭/E♭
A♭6/B♭
4.
friend to the world.
E♭
A♭6/E♭
molto rit.
Slow
E♭
A♭6/E♭
E♭add2
Ped.
Ped.

IT'S AN EASY THING TO DO

(Recycle Now Week: c. 20–26 June)

Words and Music by
Niki Davies

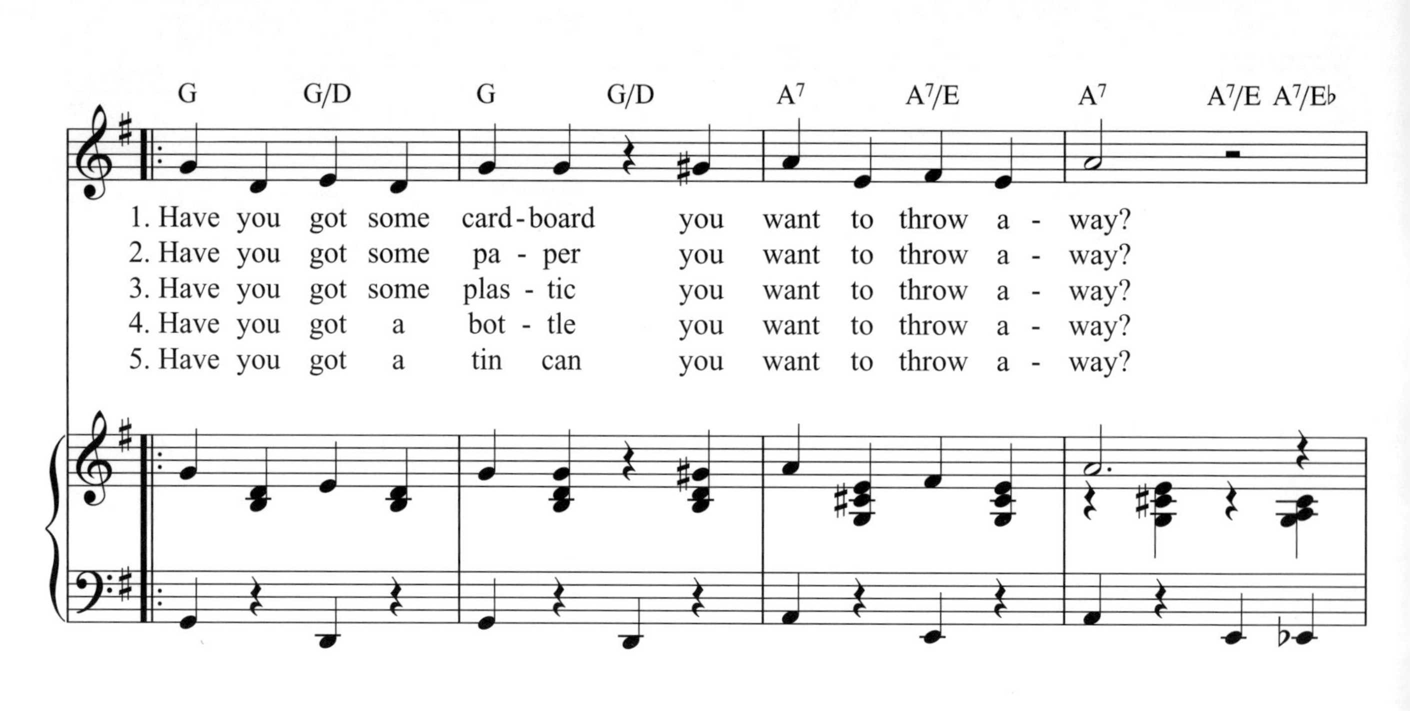

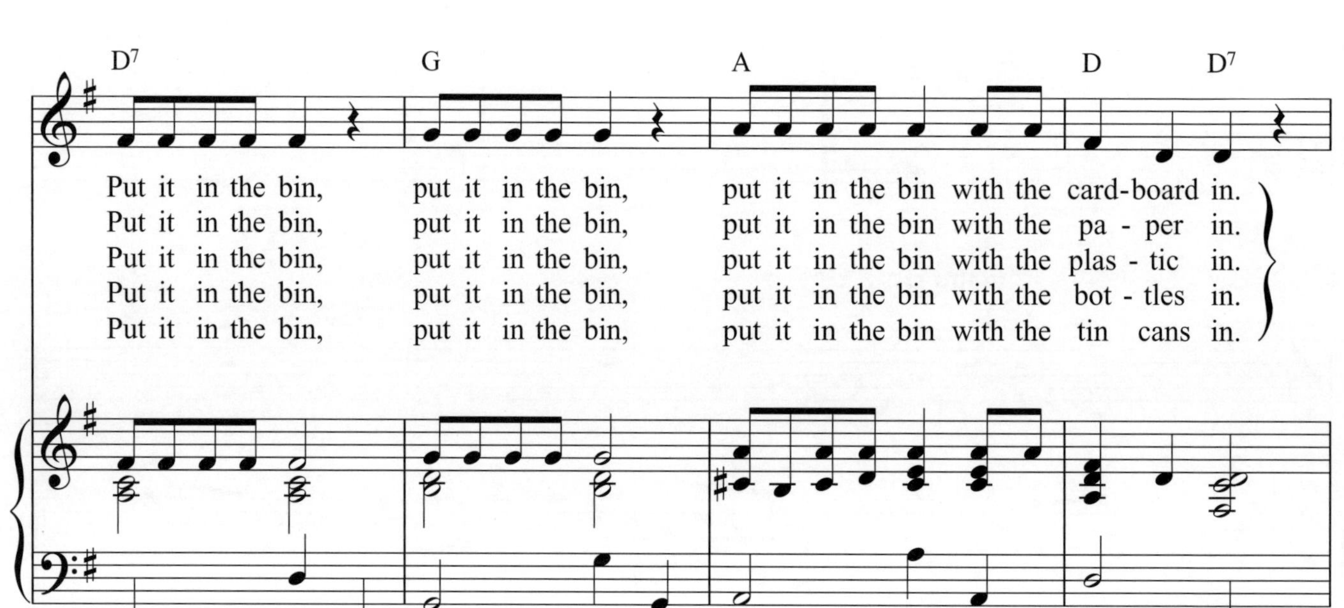

E7 A7 D7 1 – 4. G
It's an ea - sy thing to do, I re - cy - cle, so can you.
A7 Am7 C6 A7/C♯ D G/D D7
5.
D7 G G/D E7 A7
so can you. It's an ea - sy thing to do,
D7 G D C/D G/D D7 G
I re - cy - cle, so can you.

IT'S FATHER'S DAY

(June)

Words and Music by
Niki Davies

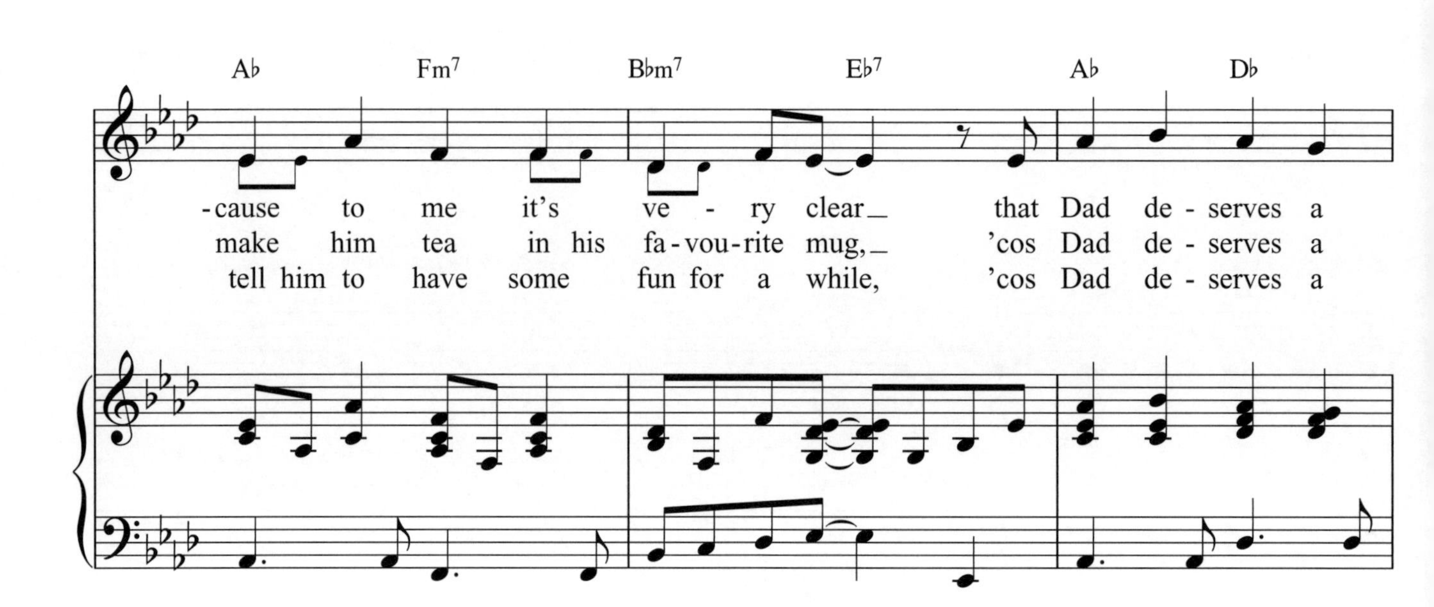

CCLI Song No. 6149565

C2/4 C7/E Fm7
Bbm7
Eb7
spe-cial day, so give him a cheer, it's Fa-ther's
spe-cial day so give him a hug, it's Fa-ther's
spe-cial day so give him a smile, it's Fa-ther's
1. 2. 3.
Ab Fm7 Bbm7 Eb7 Ab Fm7
Day.
Day.
Day.
Bbm7 Bb7/D Eb7
4.
Ab Db/Ab Ab Db/Ab Ab
Day.

Are You Ready for Some Summer Fun?

(Summer)

Words and Music by
Niki Davies

C
C6
G13
shi - ning down. The sun is shi - ning,
in the sky. The birds are fly - ing
ev - ery - where. The flowers are bloom - ing
get - ting hot. The bar - be - cue is
C
C/B♭
A7
Dm9
F/G
G7
shi - ning down, are you rea - dy for some sum - mer fun?
in the sky, are you rea - dy for some sum - mer fun?
ev - ery - where, are you rea - dy for some sum - mer fun?
get - ting hot, are you rea - dy for some sum - mer fun?
1 – 4.
5.
C6
Dm11
G7
C
G9
C
2. The
3. The
4. The
5. The

IN MY BOOK

(International Literacy Day: 8 September)

Words and Music by
Niki Davies

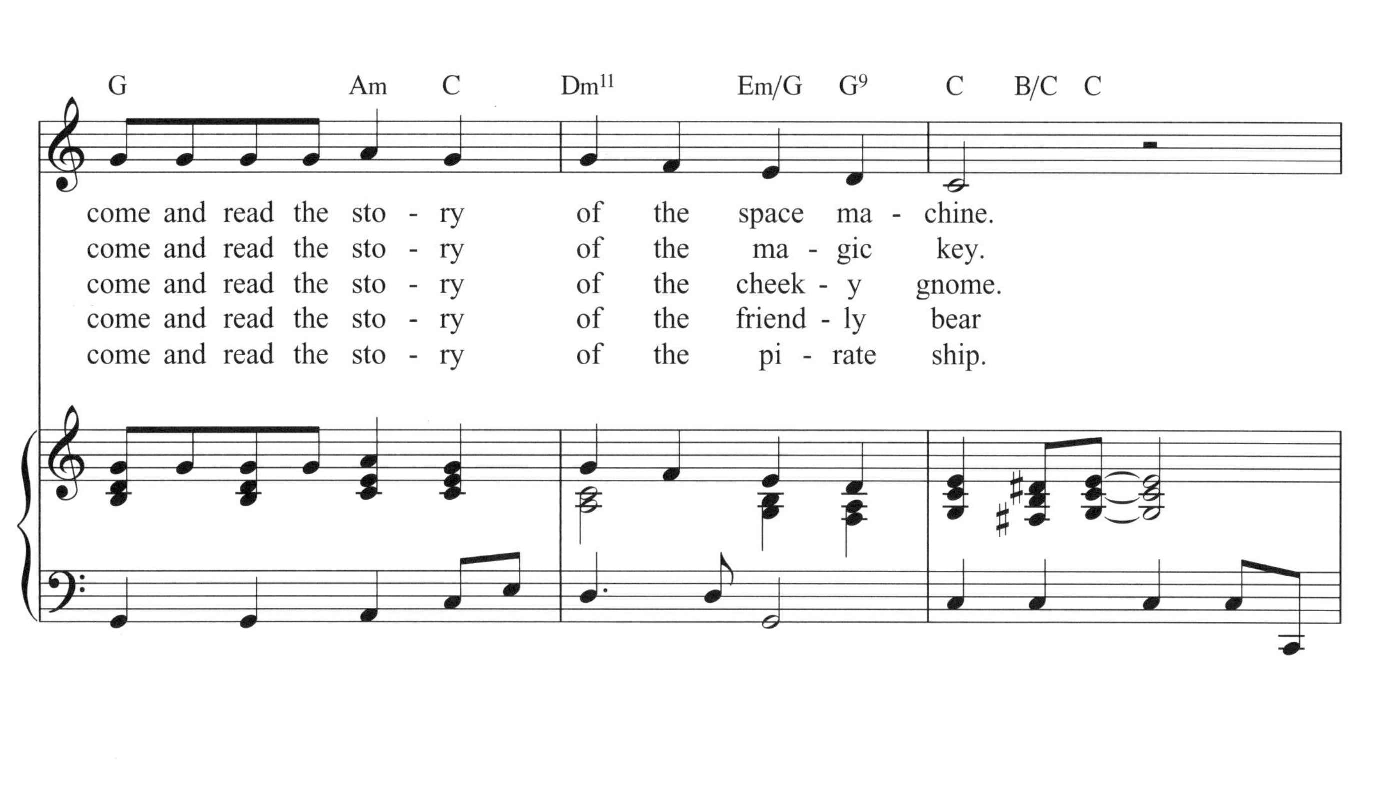
G Am C Dm11 Em/G G9 C B/C C
come and read the sto - ry of the space ma - chine.
come and read the sto - ry of the ma - gic key.
come and read the sto - ry of the cheek - y gnome.
come and read the sto - ry of the friend - ly bear
come and read the sto - ry of the pi - rate ship.

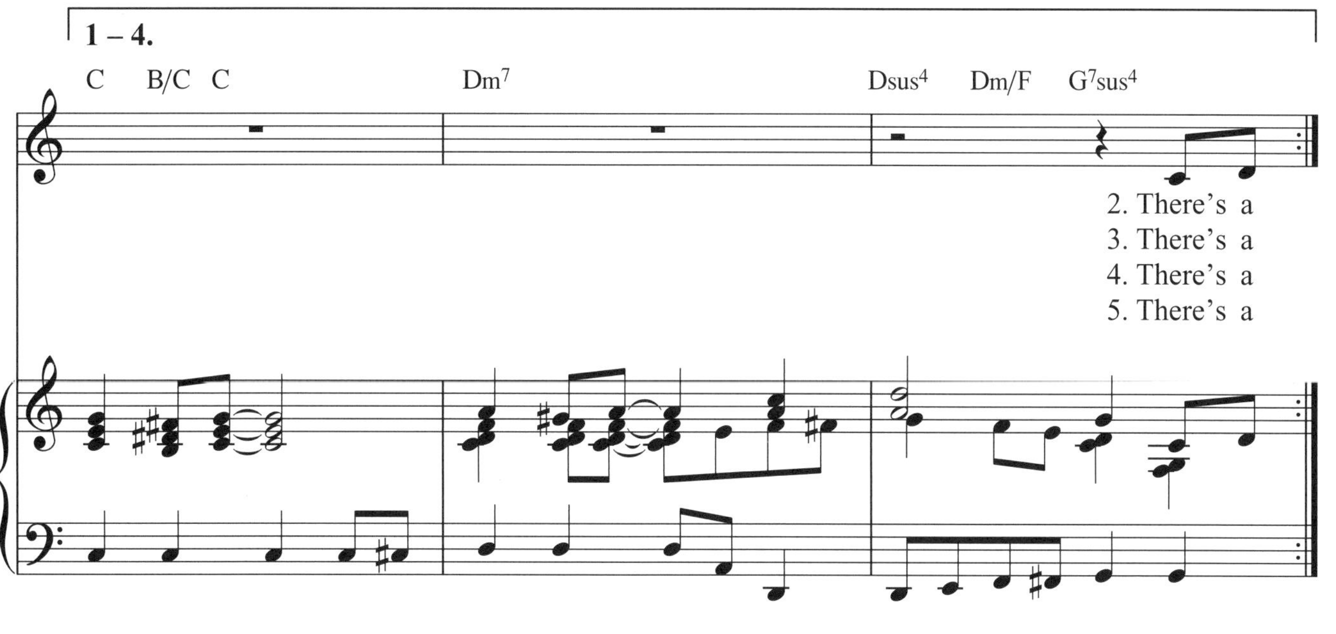
1 – 4.
C B/C C Dm7 Dsus4 Dm/F G7sus4
2. There's a
3. There's a
4. There's a
5. There's a

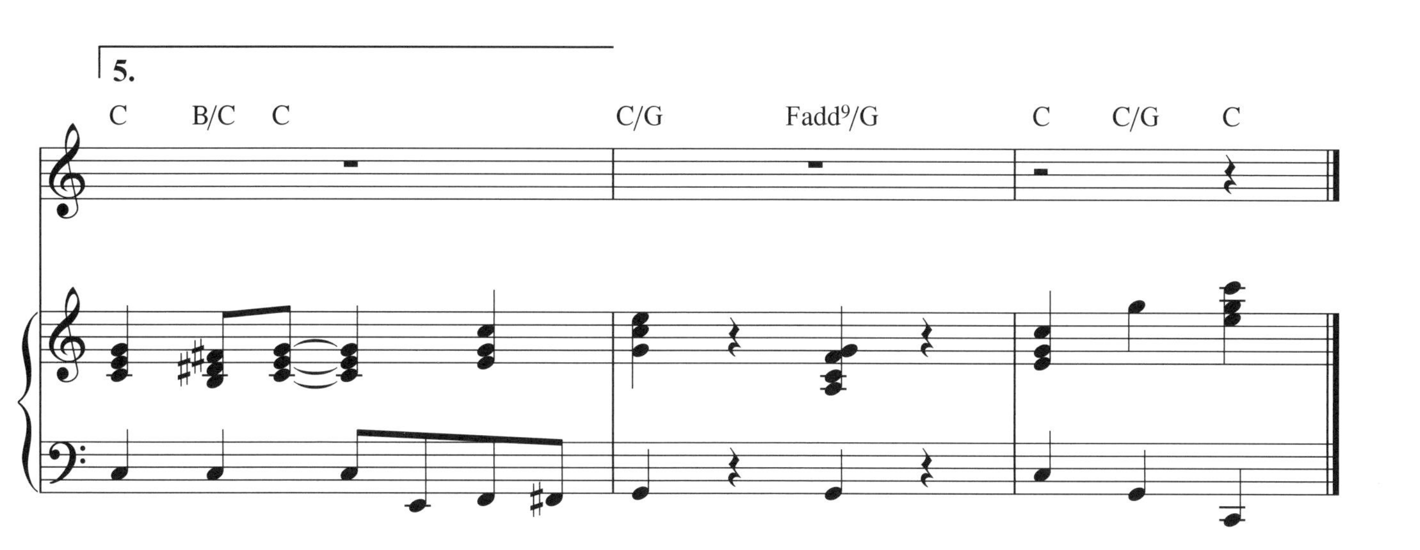
5.
C B/C C C/G Fadd9/G C C/G C

Thank You for the Harvest

(September/October)

Words and Music by
Niki Davies

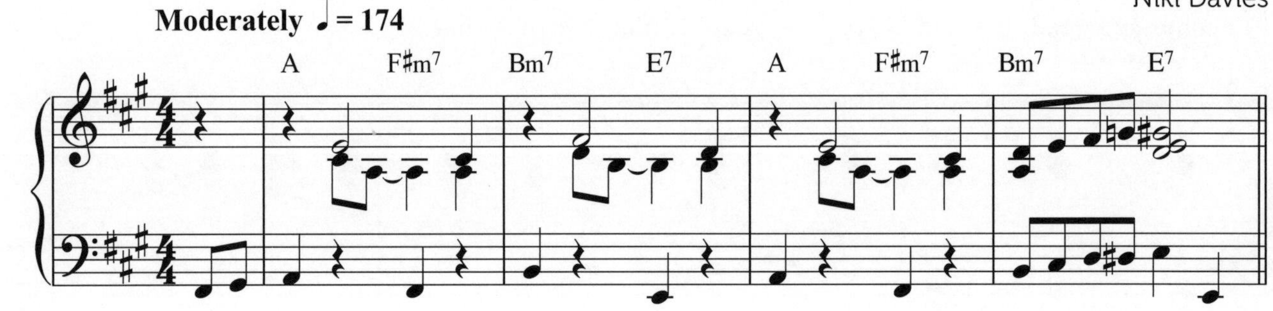

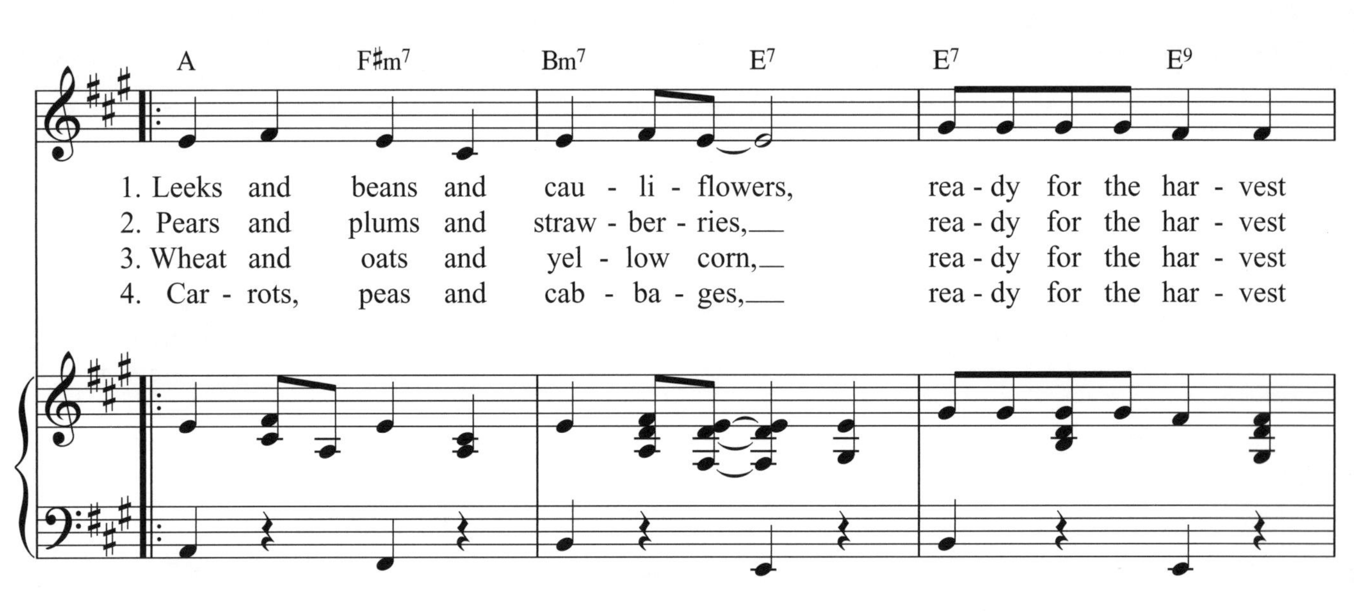

Bm11 E7 A Bm7 A/C♯ D6 Dm Aadd9 F♯m7
ripe and plump and fine. So thank you, thank you,
Bm7 E7 A6 A Bm11 A/C♯ D6 Dm Aadd9 F♯m7
thank you for the har - vest. Thank you, thank you,
To Coda
1. 2. 3.
Bm7 E7 A A/E A F♯m7 Bm9 E7
for the har - vest time.
4.
D.𝄋 al Coda
CODA
A F♯m7 Bm7 E7 A Bm7 A/C♯ A D/E A
time. So time.

Crunching Through the Leaves

(Autumn)

Words and Music by
Niki Davies

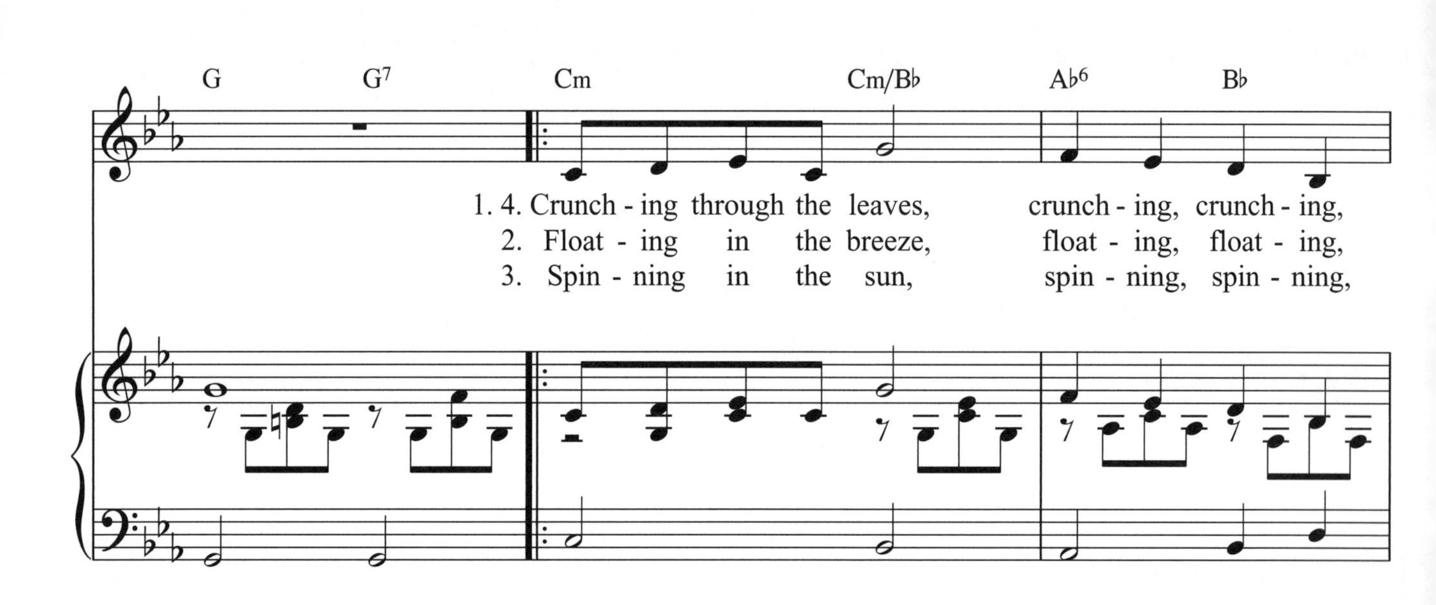

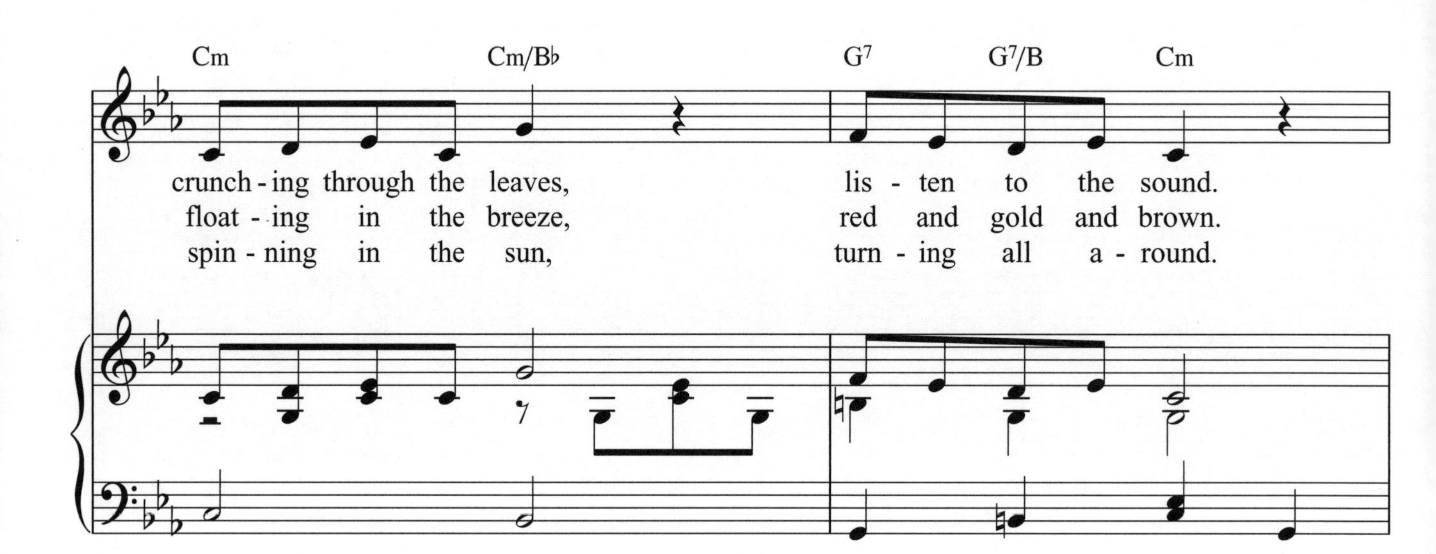

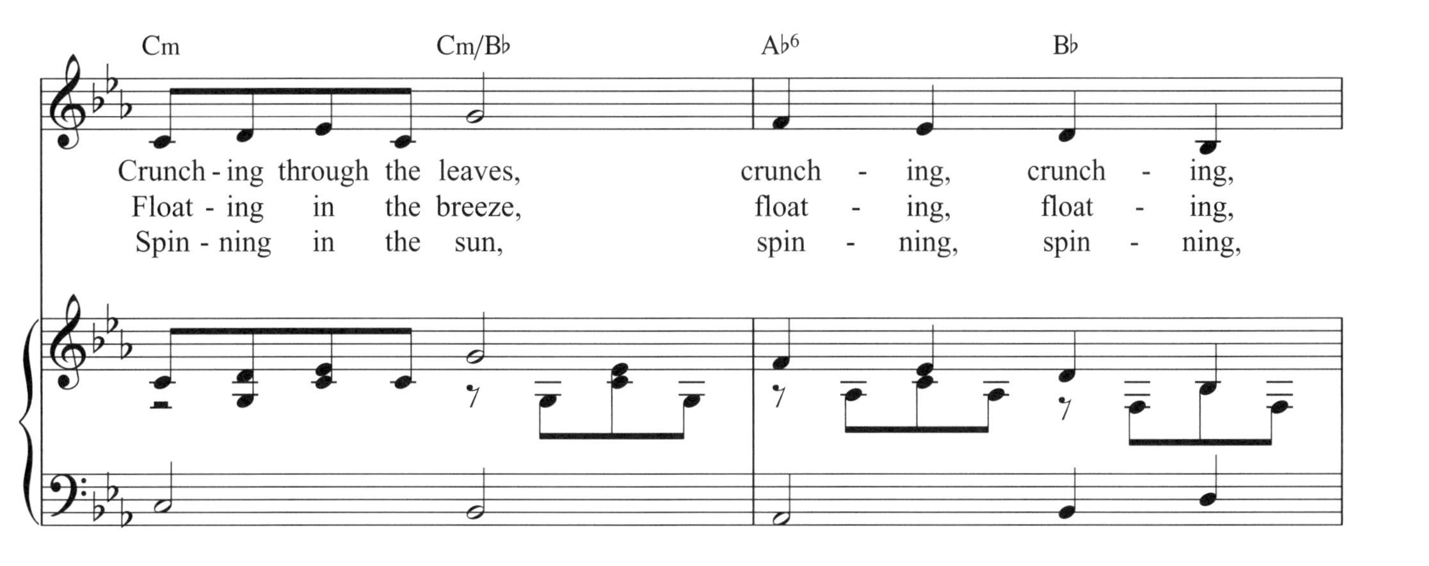
Cm
Cm/B♭
A♭6
B♭
Crunch - ing through the leaves, crunch - ing, crunch - ing,
Float - ing in the breeze, float - ing, float - ing,
Spin - ning in the sun, spin - ning, spin - ning,

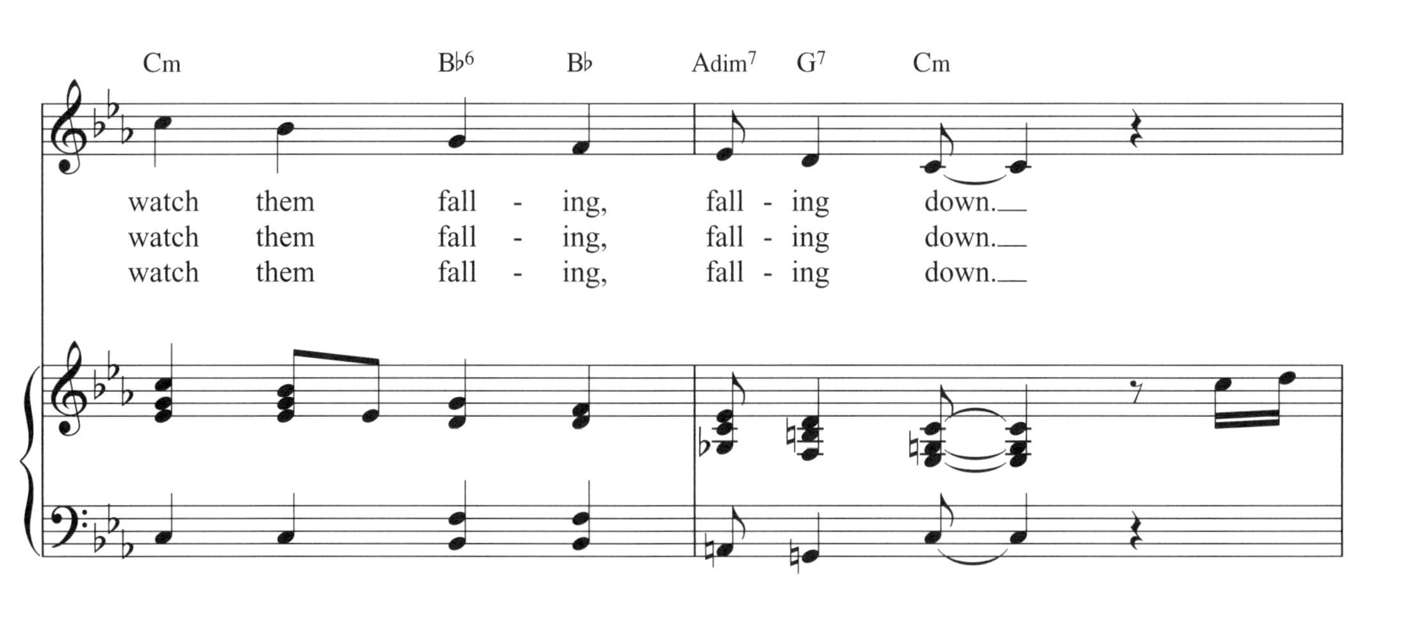
Cm
B♭6
B♭
Adim7
G7
Cm
watch them fall - ing, fall - ing down.
watch them fall - ing, fall - ing down.
watch them fall - ing, fall - ing down.

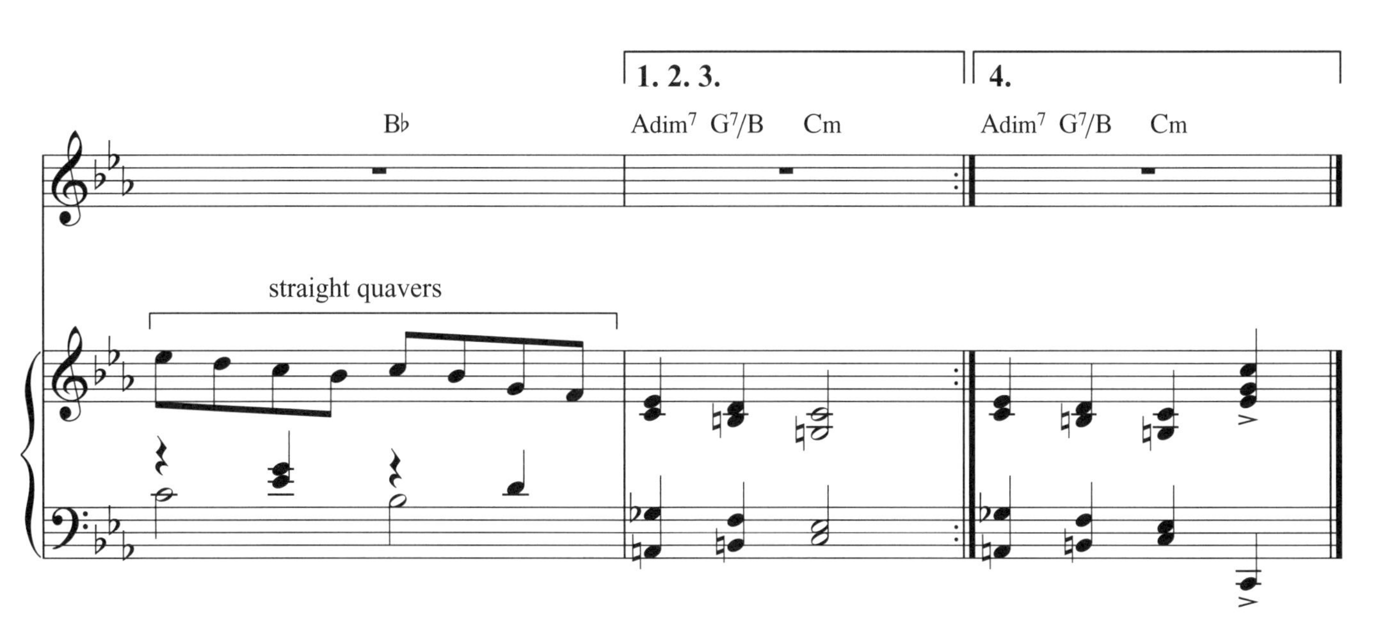
1. 2. 3.
4.
B♭
Adim7 G7/B Cm
Adim7 G7/B Cm
straight quavers

Wear a Poppy Today

(Remembrance Day: 11 November)

Words and Music by
Niki Davies

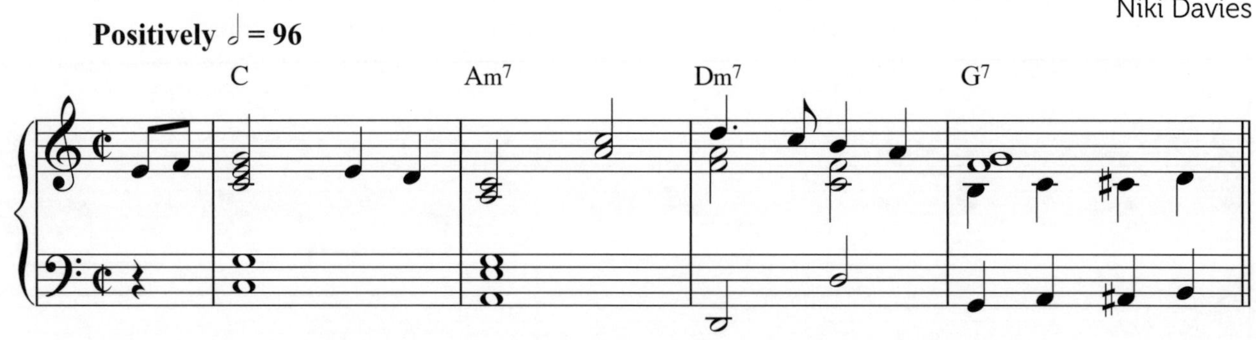

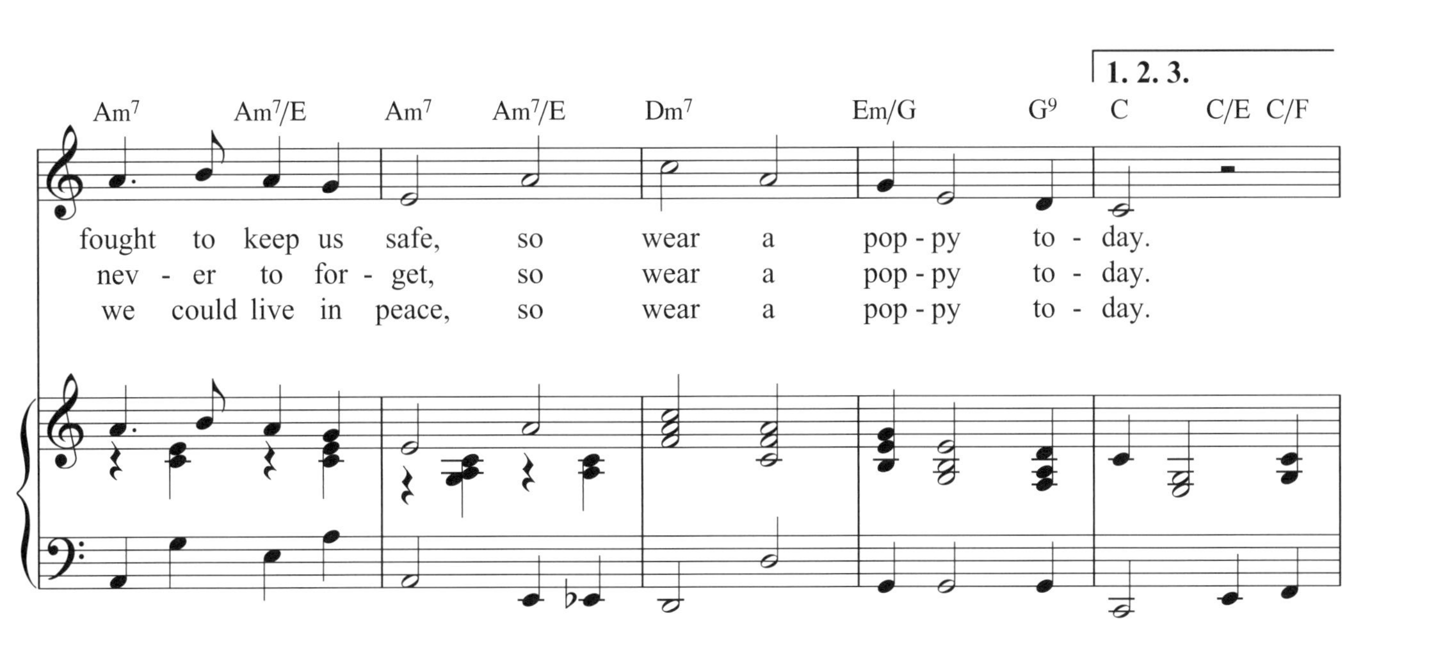
1. 2. 3.
Am7 Am7/E Am7 Am7/E Dm7 Em/G G9 C C/E C/F
fought to keep us safe, so wear a pop - py to - day.
nev - er to for - get, so wear a pop - py to - day.
we could live in peace, so wear a pop - py to - day.

F6/G F6/A F6/B C C/B Am7 Dm7 G7

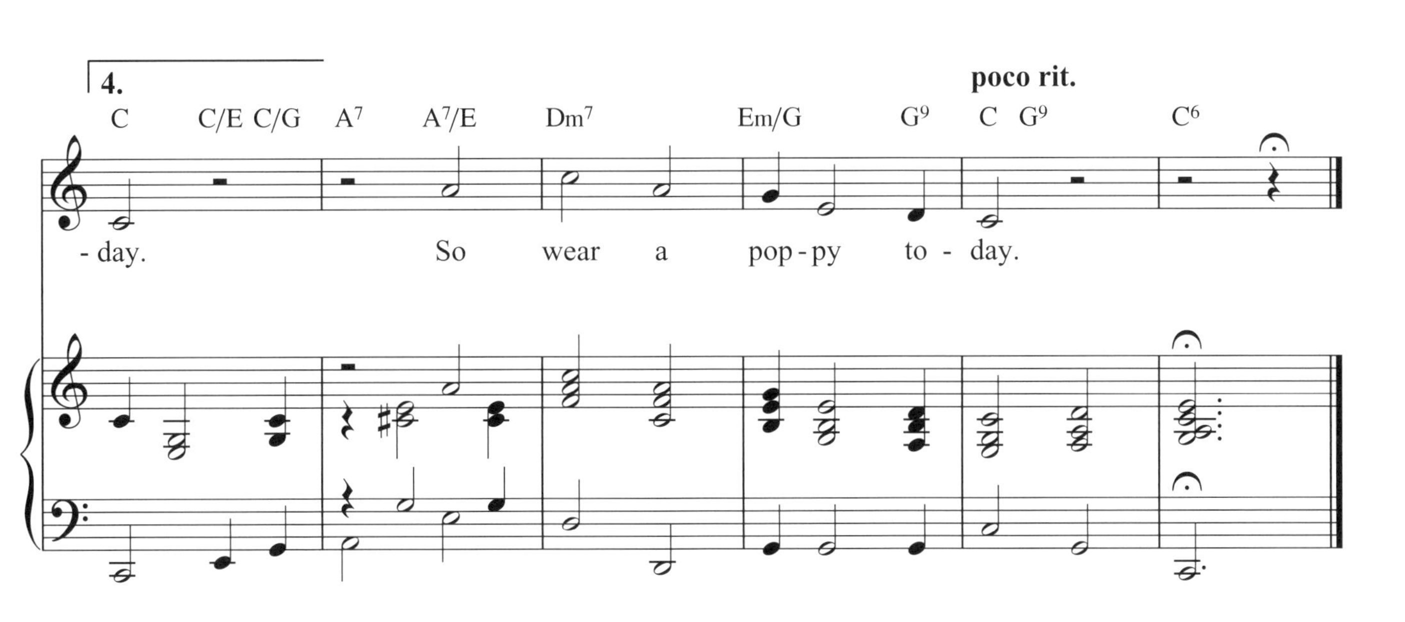
4.
poco rit.
C C/E C/G A7 A7/E Dm7 Em/G G9 C G9 C6
- day. So wear a pop - py to - day.

Give a Little Smile

(World Kindness Day: 13 November
Anti-bullying Week: c. 14–18 November)

Words and Music by
Niki Davies

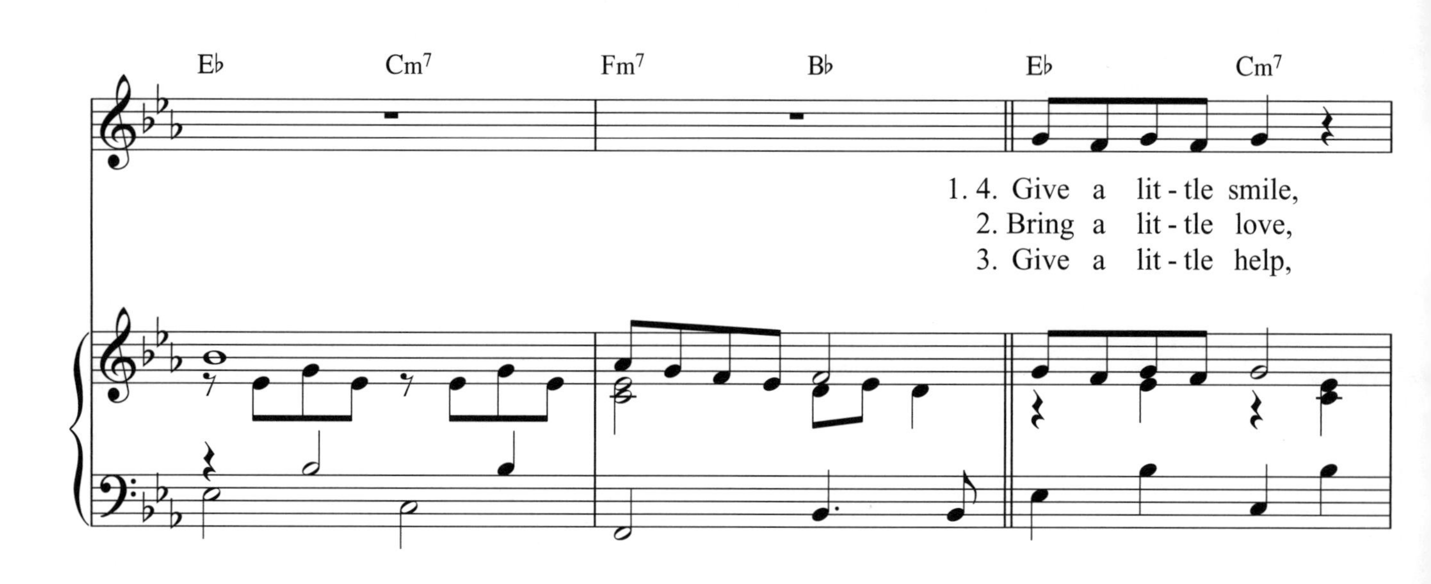

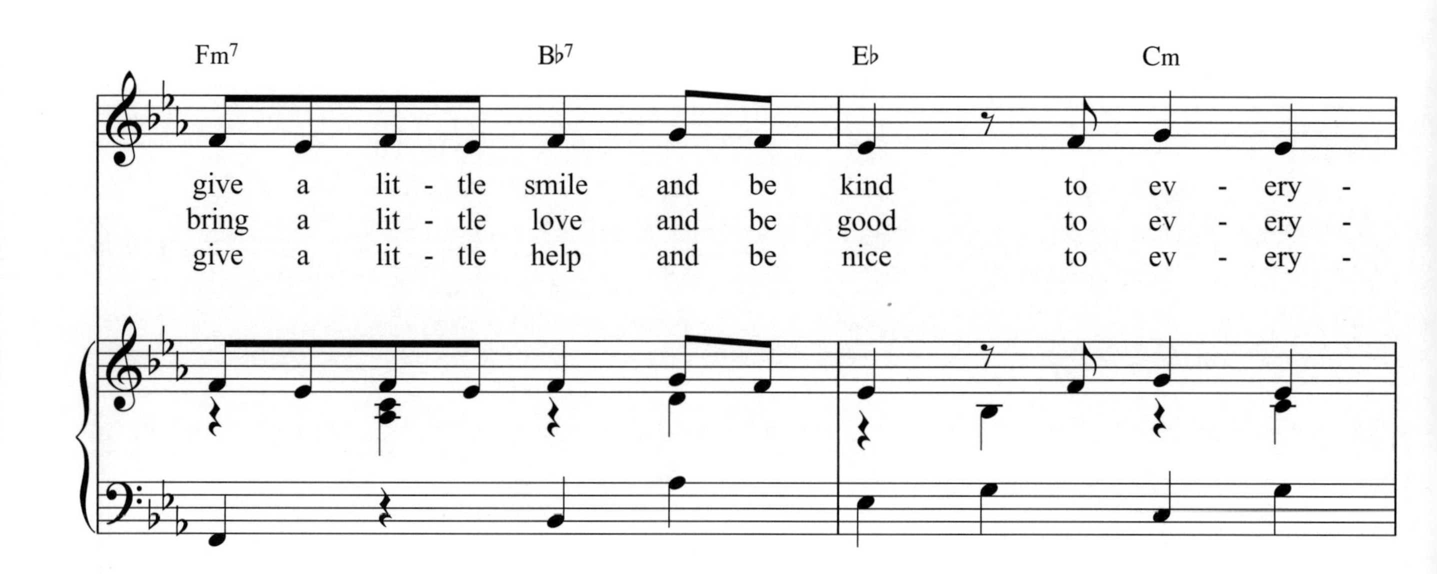

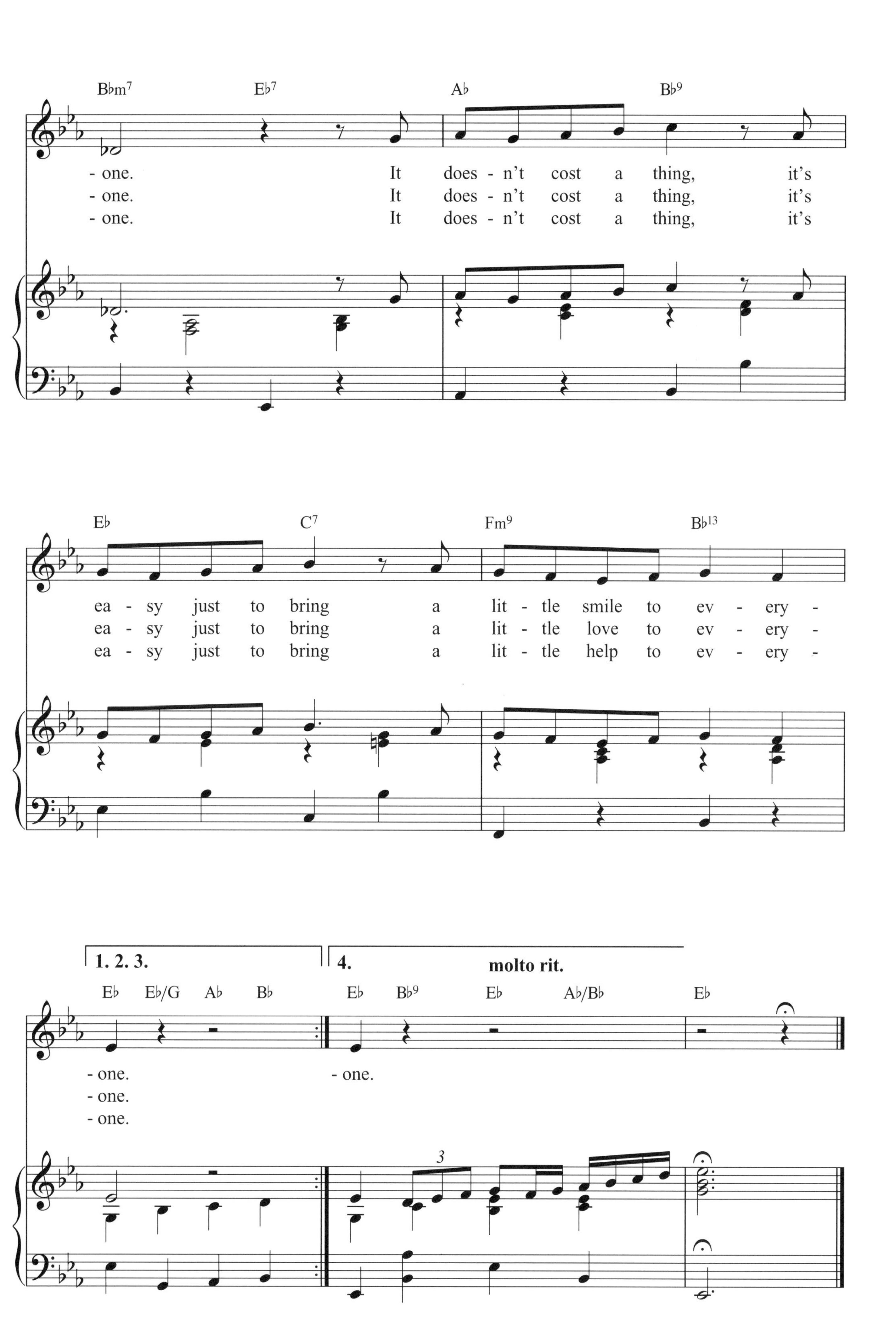
B♭m7 E♭7 A♭ B♭9
- one. It does - n't cost a thing, it's
- one. It does - n't cost a thing, it's
- one. It does - n't cost a thing, it's
E♭ C7 Fm9 B♭13
ea - sy just to bring a lit - tle smile to ev - ery -
ea - sy just to bring a lit - tle love to ev - ery -
ea - sy just to bring a lit - tle help to ev - ery -
1. 2. 3.
4.
molto rit.
E♭ E♭/G A♭ B♭
E♭ B♭9 E♭ A♭/B♭ E♭
- one.
- one.
- one.
- one.
3

Behind the Window

(Advent: December)

CCLI Song No. 6150925

F6 C7sus4 F C9 F6 F Gm7 C13
ro - bin, a lit - tle ro - bin bob - bin, be - hind my ad - vent
star shine, some spin - gle, span - gle star shine, be - hind my ad - vent
ca - mel, a lum - py, bum - py ca - mel, be - hind my ad - vent
San - ta, a jol - ly, jol - ly San - ta, be - hind my ad - vent
ba - by, a pre - cious lit - tle ba - by, be - hind my ad - vent
1 – 4.
Gm7 C9 F6 C9 F C9 G7 G7/D C B♭/C C7
ca - len - dar win - dow?
ca - len - dar win - dow?
ca - len - dar win - dow?
ca - len - dar win - dow?
ca - len - dar
5.
F6 C7 F C7 Gm9 C11 F C7 F
win - dow?
3

HAPPY CHRISTMAS!

(December)

Words and Music by
Niki Davies

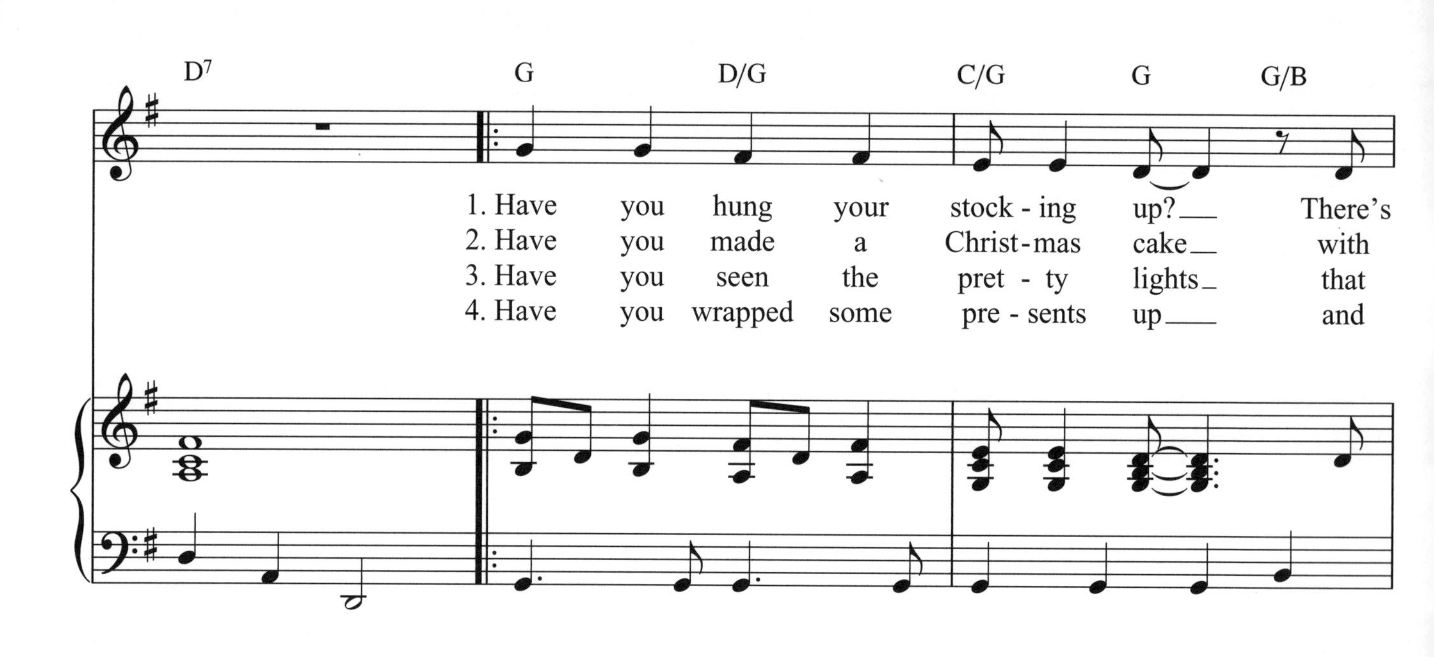

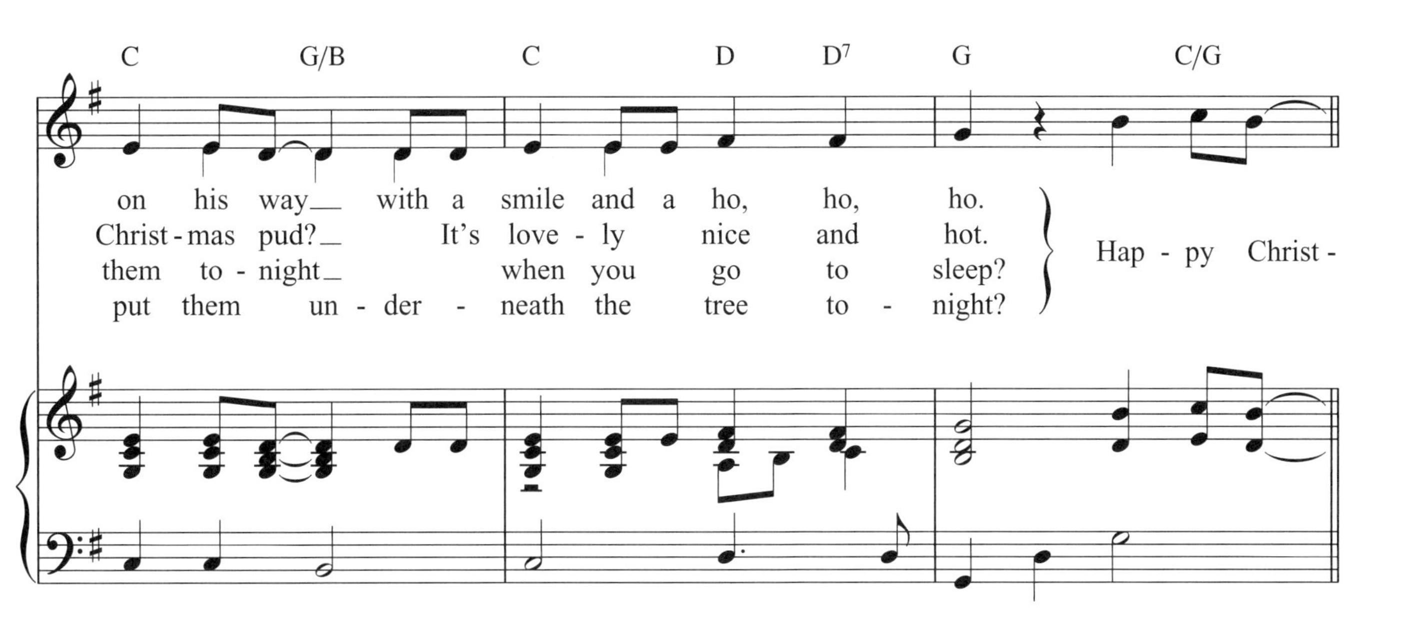
C G/B C D D7 G C/G
on his way with a smile and a ho, ho, ho.
Christ-mas pud? It's love-ly nice and hot.
them to-night when you go to sleep?
put them un-der-neath the tree to-night?
Hap-py Christ-

A9sus4 Am Em/A D7 G9sus4 D/F♯
-mas, Hap-py Christ-mas,

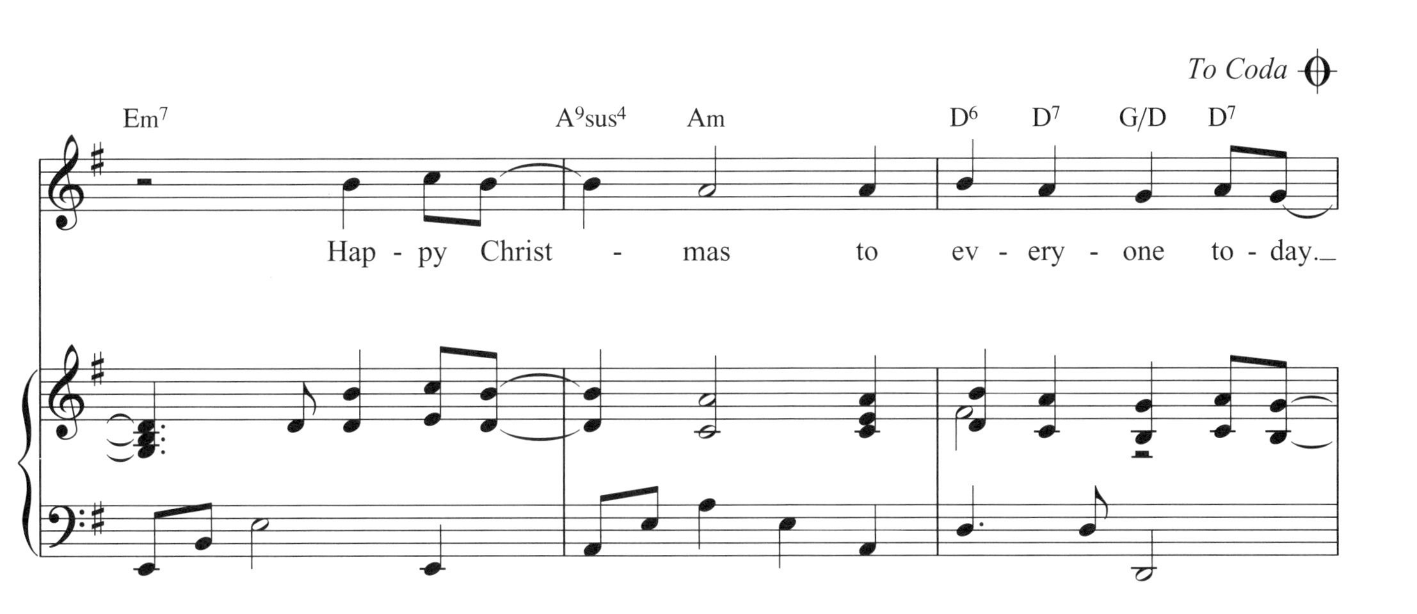
To Coda
Em7 A9sus4 Am D6 D7 G/D D7
Hap-py Christ-mas to ev-ery-one to-day.

1. 2. 3.
G
Em7
C6
D
D7
G
Em7

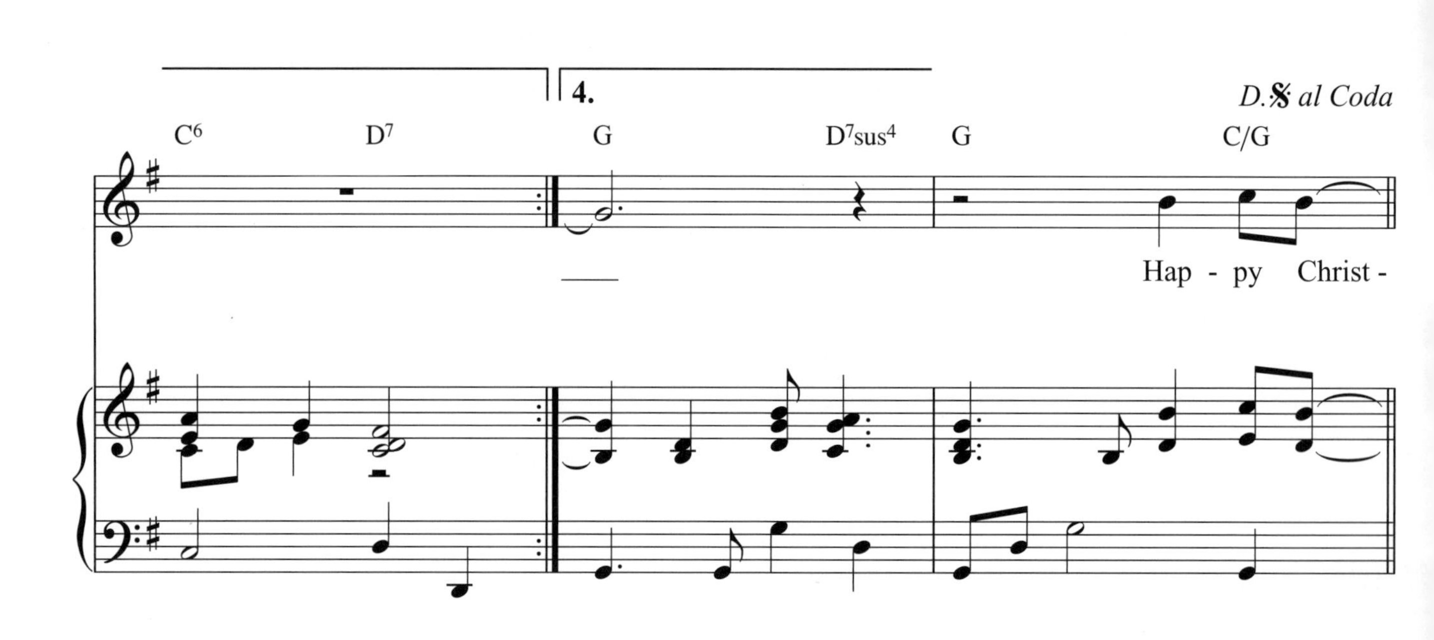
4.
D.𝄋 al Coda
C6
D7
G
D7sus4
G
C/G
Hap - py Christ -

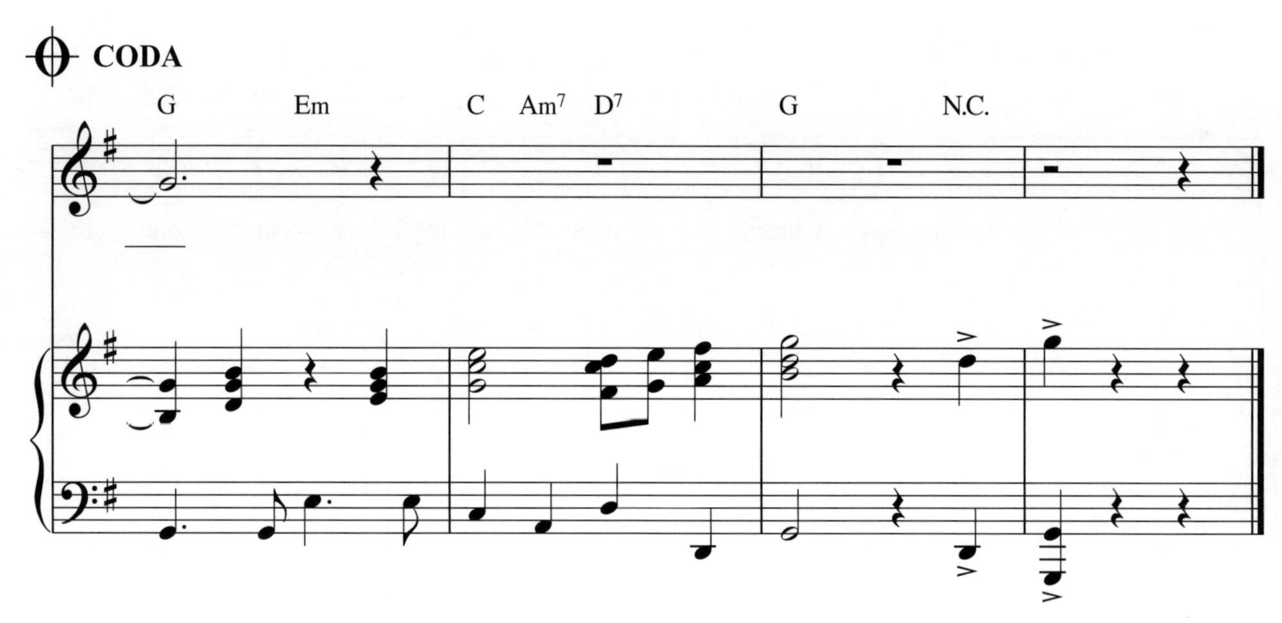
CODA
G
Em
C
Am7
D7
G
N.C.

COPYRIGHT & LICENSING - What You Need To Know

The world of copyright and licensing can seem very daunting, particularly because there is an obligation on schools to comply with copyright law. We're here to help you through the process and to keep you legal. The guidelines below explain the most common copyright and licensing issues.

Singing Songs in the Classroom

You are free to use all of the material – including songs and scripts – in the classroom for teaching purposes. If photocopying any part of the book for teaching purposes please record this usage on your school's photocopy log to ensure that you are legally protected.

Singing Songs in an Assembly or in Church

Songs may be sung in assembly without charge. In addition, the CD may be played provided that your school has a PRS licence. However, the reproduction of the lyrics and/or musical scores for use in an assembly or a church requires a licence. The following licences from Christian Copyright Licensing Limited (www.ccli.com) permit the photocopying or reproduction of song lyrics or musical scores – for example to create song sheets, overhead transparencies or to display the lyrics or music using any electronic display medium:

For UK schools: A Collective Worship Copyright Licence and a Music Reproduction Licence
For churches: A Church Copyright and Music Reproduction Licence

The following credit should be included with the lyrics:

'Reproduced by kind permission © Out of the Ark Ltd'

Please ensure that you log the songs that are used on your CCLI and MRL copy report.

Your CCLI licence also grants you permission to display the song lyrics from our Words on Screen™ CD ROMs on a whiteboard or other screen. Simply log the song titles on your copy report.

Organisations that do not hold one of the above licences should contact Out of the Ark Limited directly for permission.

Singing Songs in a Concert

If you are performing any of our songs for the public on school premises (i.e. to anyone other than pupils or staff) then royalty payments become due. Contact Out of the Ark Music directly to obtain a licence. **Please note:** There is no need to obtain a licence from the publisher if your school has an arrangement with the **Performing Rights Society (PRS)** either directly or through the local authority.

If you are performing songs at a public venue (other than on the school premises or in a church) then the performance should be logged on the venue's PRS report.

The photocopying or reproduction of song lyrics or musical scores for use in concerts – for example to create song sheets, overhead transparencies or to display the lyrics or music using any electronic display medium – requires a licence. Please contact Out of the Ark Music directly.

Making an Audio Recording or a Video of the Performance

If you wish to make an audio or video recording of your performance of any of our works please visit **www.outoftheark.com/licensing** for further information.

Copying and File-sharing

Copying Out of the Ark Music's audio CDs is not permitted without obtaining a licence from the publisher. Installation of Out of the Ark Music's audio CD tracks on to a computer is strictly forbidden without a licence – we can provide schools with a 'Learning Platform Installation Licence'. File-sharing of any of our audio tracks or CD ROM files is strictly prohibited.

For more information visit **www.outoftheark.com/licensing.**

Helpful information can be found on the following website:

A Guide to Licensing Copyright in Schools: www.outoftheark.com/licensing

And remember, we are always happy to help. For advice simply contact our customer services team:

Tel: +44 (0)20 8481 7200 Email: copyright@outoftheark.com

3-6s

SEASONAL SONG COLLECTIONS

by Niki Davies

From one of Britain's top music writers for children, this series of seasonal collections from Niki Davies provides a wonderful library of songs that are simple to learn and great fun to sing – an ideal resource for use throughout the year!

Written for nursery and reception aged children, but suitable for older children too, each book contains ten songs along with lots of ideas for further activities and curriculum links.

Each songbook package provides:

- Quality recordings of all the songs, sung by children
- Professionally arranged and produced backing tracks
- Piano music with melody, lyrics and guitar chords
- Teachers' notes/curriculum links for The Foundation Stage

IT MUST BE SPRING!

With ten brand new songs for spring-time and other times of the year, this songbook will be an instant hit with younger children.

Titles include:

- It must be spring!
- Somebody's waking up
- It's Mother's Day
- Wet, wet, wet!
- Where did the pancake go?
- A tiny seed was sleeping

HAPPY SUN HIGH

A superb collection of songs for summer and throughout the year, this book includes ten enchanting songs to brighten up everyone's day whatever the weather!

Titles include:

- Come with me to the beach
- Sunglasses
- Caterpillar
- Steam train
- Picnic
- Lying in the daisies

IT'S TIME TO FLY

Children will adore these ten original songs for autumn, with words and melodies that beautifully capture the changes of the season.

Titles include:

- One, two, three little acorns
- The owl
- Pumpkin head
- Mr Scarecrow
- Autumn leaves
- Under the harvest moon

IT'S WINTER TIME

Providing plenty of material for those winter days, with songs about frosty mornings, keeping warm and Christmas preparations, this book is an ideal supplementary resource for any winter term projects.

Titles include:

- Marching in the snow
- Snowdrop
- Put your coat on
- Jack Frost
- Mister Wind
- Socks

Out of the Ark Music, Units F1 & F2, Kingsway Business Park,
Oldfield Road, Hampton, Middlesex TW12 2HD, UK
Telephone: +44 (0)20 8481 7200 Fax: +44 (0)20 8941 5548
Email: info@outoftheark.com
www.outoftheark.com